NUMERICAL REASONING:

Quick Fire Questions

Multiple Choice

Book 1

Tests 1 - 10

How to use this pack to make the most of 11 plus exam preparation

It is important to remember that for 11 plus exams there is no national syllabus, no pass mark and no retake option! It is therefore vitally important that your child is fully primed in order so that they perform to the best of their ability and give themselves the best possible chance on the day.

Unlike similar publications, the **First Past the Post®** series uniquely assesses your child's performance relative to a peer group, thus helping to identify areas for improvement and further practice.

Numerical Reasoning

This collection of tests is representative of the short numerical reasoning section of contemporary multi-discipline 11 plus exams, including those set by CEM (Durham University). One paper usually has a section of long worded numerical reasoning problems and the other contains short, quick fire questions more akin to traditional maths. This publication addresses the latter. The suggested time for each paper is provided based on classroom testing sessions held at our centre.

Never has it been more useful to learn from mistakes!

Students can improve by as much as 15% not only by focused practice, but also by targeting any weak areas.

How to manage your child's own practice

To get the most up-to-date information, visit our website, www.elevenplusexams.co.uk, the largest UK online resource with over 65,000 webpages and a forum administered by a select group of experienced moderators.

About the authors

The Eleven Plus Exams **First Past the Post®** series has been created by a team of experienced tutors and authors from leading British universities including Oxford and Cambridge.

Published by University of Buckingham Press.

With special thanks to the children who tested our material at the Eleven Plus Exams centre in Harrow.

Please note the UBP is not associated with CEM or The University of Durham in any way. This book does not include any official questions and it is not endorsed by CEM or The University of Durham.
CEM, Centre for Evaluation and Monitoring, Durham University and *The University of Durham* are all trademarks of The University of Durham.

ISBN: 9781908684653

About Us

ElevenPlusExams is the UK's largest website offering a vast amount of information and advice, a moderated online forum, books, downloadable materials and online services to enhance your child's chances of success in the demanding selective schools entrance exams, namely the 11+ and common entrance exams.

The company also provides specialist 11+ tuition and is a supplier of online services to schools.

ElevenPlusExams is recognised as a trusted and authoritative source of information and advice. It has been quoted in numerous national newspapers (including The Telegraph, The Sunday Observer, The Daily Mail, The Sunday Telegraph), BBC Radio and national television (BBC1 and Channel 4).

Set up in 2004, the website grew from an initial 20 webpages to more than 65,000 today and has been visited by millions of parents.

The website gives parents impartial advice on preparation, techniques, 11+ exams in their area and preparation material based on actual experience. The forum is the largest for 11+ in the UK, and is moderated by over 20 experts including parents, experienced tutors and authors who collectively provide support both before the exams, and for those parents who are also unfortunate enough to have to appeal the decisions.

Visit our website to benefit from the wealth of information and advice and see why we are the market's leading 'one-stop-shop' for all your eleven plus needs.

✓ Comprehensive quality content and advice written by 11+ experts

✓ 11+ Online Shop supplying a wide range of practice books, e-papers, software and apps

✓ UK's largest online 11+ Forum moderated by experts

✓ Lots of FREE practice papers to download

✓ Professional tuition services optimising state of the art technology

✓ Short Revision courses

✓ Year long 11+ courses

✓ Mock exams tailored to mirror those of the main examining bodies

Other titles in the First Past The Post® Series

11 + Essentials CEM Style Practice Tests

Verbal Reasoning: Cloze Tests
Book 1
9781908684288

Verbal Reasoning: Cloze Tests
Book 2
9781908684356

Verbal Reasoning: Grammar and
Spelling Multiple Choice Books 1 & 2
9781908684646 | 9781908684790

Verbal Reasoning: Vocabulary
Multiple Choice Books 1 & 2
9781908684639 | 9781908684783

Numerical Reasoning: Multi-part
(Standard) Books 1 & 2
9781908684301 | 9781908684363

Numerical Reasoning: Multi-part
(Multiple Choice) Books 1 & 2
9781908684769 | 9781908684776
NEW for 2016

Numerical Reasoning: Quick-fire
(Standard) Books 1 & 2
9781908684431 | 9781908684448

Numerical Reasoning: Quick-fire
(Multiple Choice) Books 1 & 2
9781908684653 | 9781908684752
NEW for 2016

English: Comprehensions
Book 1
9781908684295

English: Comprehensions
Book 2
9781908684486

3D Non-Verbal Reasoning
Book 1
9781908684318

3D Non-Verbal Reasoning
Book 2
9781908684479

Mental Arithmetic
Book 1

9781908684462

Numerical Reasoning:
Worded Problems

Book 1

9781908684806

Maths Dictionary
9781908684493

NEW for 2016

11 + Practice Paper Packs

Non-Verbal Reasoning
Practice Papers
9781908684134

English
Practice Papers
9781908684103

Verbal Reasoning
Practice Papers
9781908684127

Mathematics
Practice Papers
9781908684110

Contents Page

This workbook comprises ten tests, made up of twenty short questions each. Each test should take six minutes to complete.

Once you have completed each test and marked it using the answers at the back you can anonymously go online and compare your child's performance relative to peers who have completed the same test(s) using our 11+ Peer Compare System™.

Register at http://peercompare.elevenplusexams.co.uk/

and then activate the access code printed on the inside cover.

Instructions

In this book there are options given from which to choose answers, such as the one below:

A	B	C	D	E
4.6%	6%	5%	3.2%	4.1%

When circling your chosen option, only circle the letter above of the option. If you circle both the option letter and the answer, this may cover the answer and make it unclear for marking.

INCORRECT

A	B	C	D	E
4.6%	6%	5%	3.2%	4.1%

CORRECT

If you want to change your answer, either rub it out or put a line across your original answer and circle the new answer.

A	B	C	D	E
4.6%	6%	5%	3.2%	4.1%

INCORRECT

A	B	C	D	E
4.6%	6%	5%	3.2%	4.1%

CORRECT

A	B	C	D	E
4.6%	6%	5%	3.2%	4.1%

CORRECT

Your Handy Glossary

Learn the meanings of the terms listed below to expand your mathematical vocabulary.

Apothem - a line segment from the centre of a regular polygon to the midpoint of one of its sides.

Bearing - an angle given in three figures that is measured clockwise from the north direction, e.g. 025°.

BIDMAS - an acronym for Brackets, Indices, Division and Multiplication, and Addition and Subtraction. It is the agreed order of operations used to clarify which should be performed first in a given expression.

Bimodal - when a collection of data has two modes, e.g. if the dataset is: {1, 1, 1, 2, 4, 5, 5, 5}, the two modes are 1 and 5.

Bisect - to divide into two equal parts.

Coefficient - a constant that is placed before a variable in an algebraic expression, e.g. in the term $4x$, the coefficient is 4.

Complementary angles - two angles are complementary if they add up to 90°.

Cube number - a number produced when a digit is multiplied by itself twice, e.g. 1, 8, 27, 64.

Edge - a line segment that joins two vertices of a 2D shape, or a line segment at which two faces meet in a 3D shape.

Enlargement - a type of transformation in which the size of an object is changed whilst the ratio of the lengths of its sides stays the same.

Equidistant - the same distance from a common point.

Face - an individual surface of a 3D shape.

Fair - a fair item or event is free from bias.

Gallon - a unit of volume used for measuring liquids, equal to 8 pints or 4.55 litres.

Gradient - a gradient is a measure of the steepness of a straight line.

Highest common factor (HCF) - the largest number that is a factor of two or more given numbers, e.g. 5 is the highest common factor of 10 and 15.

Imperial units - the system of units first defined in the British Weights and Measures Act, e.g. 3 feet.

Inscribe - to draw a shape within another so that their boundaries touch but do not intersect.

Integer - a whole number, i.e. not a decimal or a fraction.

Isosceles trapezium - a trapezium which has one line of symmetry, two pairs of equal angles and one pair of parallel sides.

Leap year - a calendar year occurring every four years, totalling 366 days and including the 29th February, e.g. the year 2012 was a leap year.

Lowest common multiple (LCM) - the smallest number that is a multiple of two or more given numbers, e.g. 6 is the lowest common multiple of 2 and 3.

Metric units - The system of units based on multiples of 10, e.g. millimetre (mm), centimetre (cm) or metre (m).

Net - a 2D pattern that can be cut out and folded to make a 3D shape.

Parallel - lines that run side-by-side, always the same distance apart and never crossing, even if they are extended.

Perimeter - the total distance around the outside of a 2D shape.

Perpendicular - two lines are perpendicular if they intersect at an angle of 90° to each other.

Polygon - a 2D shape with three or more straight sides and no curved sides, e.g. triangle, pentagon, hexagon.

Polyhedron - a 3D shape with polygonal faces, e.g. triangular pyramid or octahedron.

Prime factor - one of a collection of prime numbers whose product is a particular number, i.e. a factor that is also a prime number.

Prime number - an integer greater than 1 that has no whole factors other than 1 and itself, e.g. 2, 3, 5.

Prism - a solid 3D shape with two identical, parallel end faces that are connected by flat sides.

Pyramid - a solid 3D shape whose base is a polygon and which has triangular faces that meet at the top at a single vertex, e.g. square pyramid.

Quadrilateral - a 2D shape with four straight sides. Quadrilaterals are polygons.

Reflective symmetry - a shape or an object has reflective symmetry if an imaginary line can be drawn that divides the shape into two, so that one half is a reflection of the other.

Regular - a regular polygon has sides of equal length.

Remainder - a number that is left over after division.

Rotational symmetry - a shape or an object has rotational symmetry if it can be rotated but still seems to have the same original position.

Scalene - a scalene triangle has sides of unequal lengths.

Sequence - a list of numbers or objects in a particular order defined by a specific pattern.

Square number - a number produced when a digit is multiplied by itself once, e.g. 1, 4, 9 or 16.

Supplementary angles - two angles are supplementary if they add up to 180°.

Triangle - a 2D shape with three straight sides. Triangles are polygons.

Triangular number - a figurate number that can be represented by a regular triangular arrangement of equally spaced points, e.g. 1, 3, 6: ● ⚬⚬ ⚬⚬⚬

Vertex - a point at which two or more straight lines meet.

Place Value

The numerical value of a digit in a number. For example, in the number 1234.567, the digit 3 has a place value of tens.

1	2	3	4	.	5	6	7
thousands	hundreds	tens	units	decimal point	tenths	hundredths	thousandths

Special Numbers

	1st	2nd	3rd	4th	5th	6th	7th	8th	9th	10th	11th	12th	13th	14th	15th	16th	17th	18th	19th	20th
Even	2	4	6	8	10	12	14	16	18	20	22	24	26	28	30	32	34	36	38	40
Odd	1	3	5	7	9	11	13	15	17	19	21	23	25	27	29	31	33	35	37	39
Square	1	4	9	16	25	36	49	64	81	100	121	144	169	196	225	256	289	324	361	400
Cube	1	8	27	64	125	216	343	512	729	1000	1331	1728	2197	2744	3375	4096	4913	5832	6859	8000
Triangular	1	3	6	10	15	21	28	36	45	55	66	78	91	105	120	136	153	171	190	210
Prime	2	3	5	7	11	13	17	19	23	29	31	37	41	43	47	53	59	61	67	71
Fibonacci	1	1	2	3	5	8	13	21	34	55	89	144	233	377	610	987	1597	2584	4181	6765

Equivalent Decimals, Fractions & Percentages

Percentage	5%	10%	15%	20%	25%	30%	35%	40%	45%	50%	55%	60%	65%	70%	75%	80%	85%	90%	95%	100%	150%
Fraction	$\frac{1}{20}$	$\frac{1}{10}$	$\frac{3}{20}$	$\frac{1}{5}$	$\frac{1}{4}$	$\frac{3}{10}$	$\frac{7}{20}$	$\frac{2}{5}$	$\frac{9}{20}$	$\frac{1}{2}$	$\frac{11}{20}$	$\frac{3}{5}$	$\frac{13}{20}$	$\frac{7}{10}$	$\frac{3}{4}$	$\frac{4}{5}$	$\frac{17}{20}$	$\frac{9}{10}$	$\frac{19}{20}$	$\frac{1}{1}$	$\frac{3}{2}$
Decimal	0.05	0.1	0.15	0.2	0.25	0.3	0.35	0.4	0.45	0.5	0.55	0.6	0.65	0.7	0.75	0.8	0.85	0.9	0.95	1	1.5

Mathematical Symbols

+	addition sign
−	subtraction sign
×	multiplication sign
÷	division sign
±	positive or negative
=	equals sign
<	less than
>	greater than
≈	approximately equal to
≤	less than or equal to
≥	greater than or equal to
≠	not equal to
a^2	squared number
a^3	cubed number
%	per cent
$\sqrt{a}$	square root
$\sqrt[3]{a}$	cubed root
$\dot{a}$	recurring number
$a:b$	ratio
$a°$	degrees
$\bar{a}$	mean
(x, y)	coordinates
∟	right angle
$\binom{x}{y}$	column vector (column matrix)
a/b	fraction
$\{a, b\}$	dataset
π	pi

Equivalent Periods of Time

1 minute	60 seconds
1 hour	60 minutes
1 day	24 hours
1 week	7 days
1 year	12 months (365 days)
1 leap year	366 days
1 decade	10 years
1 century	100 years
1 millennium	1,000 years

Roman Numerals

When a symbol appears after a numerically larger number, it is added, but if the symbol appears before a numerically larger number, it is subtracted.

1	I		40	XL
2	II		50	L
3	III		60	LX
4	IV		70	LXX
5	V		80	LXXX
6	VI		90	XC
7	VII		100	C
8	VIII		200	CC
9	IX		300	CCC
10	X		400	CD
20	XX		500	D
30	XXX		1,000	M

Time Conversion

24-hour clock	12-hour clock
00:00	12.00am
01:00	1.00am
02:00	2.00am
03:00	3.00am
04:00	4.00am
05:00	5.00am
06:00	6.00am
07:00	7.00am
08:00	8.00am
09:00	9.00am
10:00	10.00am
11:00	11.00am
12:00	12.00pm
13:00	1.00pm
14:00	2.00pm
15:00	3.00pm
16:00	4.00pm
17:00	5.00pm
18:00	6.00pm
19:00	7.00pm
20:00	8.00pm
21:00	9.00pm
22:00	10.00pm
23:00	11.00pm

Units of Measurement

		Metric system		Imperial system		
	Units	Conversion	Units	Conversion	Metric approximation
Mass	milligram (mg)	1mg = 0.1cg = 0.001g	ounce (oz)	1oz = $^1/_{16}$ lb	1oz ≈ 28g
	centigram (cg)	1cg = 10mg = 0.01g	pound (lb)	1lb = 16oz	1lb ≈ 0.45kg
	gram (g)	1g = 100cg = 0.001kg	stone (st)	1st = 14lb	1st ≈ 6kg
	kilogram (kg)	1kg = 1000g = 0.001t	ton	1 ton = 160st	1 ton ≈ 0.91 tonne
	tonne (t)	1t = 1,000,000g = 1000kg			
Length	millimetre (mm)	1mm = 0.1cm = 0.001m	inch (in or ")	1in = $^1/_{12}$ ft	1in ≈ 25mm
	centimetre (cm)	1cm = 10mm = 0.01m	foot (ft or ')	1ft = 12in	1ft ≈ 30cm
	metre (m)	1m = 100cm = 0.001km	yard (yd)	1yd = 3ft	1yd ≈ 91cm
	kilometre (km)	1km = 100,000cm = 1000m	mile	1 mile = 1760yd	1 mile ≈ 1.6km
Capacity	millilitre (ml)	1ml = 0.1cl = 0.001l = 1cm^3	fluid ounce (fl. oz)	1fl. oz = $^1/_{20}$ pt	1fl. oz ≈ 28ml
	centilitre (cl)	1cl = 10ml = 100l = 10cm^3	pint (pt)	1pt = 20fl. Oz	1pt ≈ 0.57l
	litre (l)	1l = 0.01cl = 0.001kl = 1000cm^3	gallon (gal)	1gal = 8pt	1gal ≈ 4.5l
	kilolitre (kl)	1kl = 1000l = 1,000,000cm^3			

Types of Angles

Zero angle:
Equivalent to 0°.

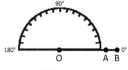

The angle AOB is an example of a zero angle.

Acute angle:
An angle smaller than 90°, but greater than 0°.

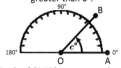

Angle $c°$ (AOB) is an example of an acute angle.

Right angle:
An angle of 90°.

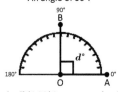

Angle $d°$ (AOB) is an example of a right angle.

Obtuse angle:
An angle between 90° and 180°.

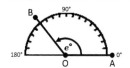

Angle $e°$ (AOB) is an example of an obtuse angle.

Flat angle:
The angle formed on a straight line, equal to 180°

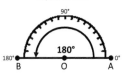

The angle AOB is an example of a flat angle.

Reflex angle:
An angle above 180° but below 360°.

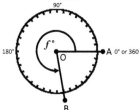

Angle $f°$ (AOB) is an example of a reflex angle.

Full rotation:
A full turn equal to 360°.

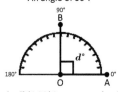

Pairs of Angles

Alternate angles:
The angles on opposite sides of a transversal between two parallel lines.

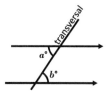

Alternate angles are always equal; i.e. $a° = b°$.

Complementary angles:
Two angles that add up to 90°.

Since $a° + b° = 90°$, they are complementary.

Supplementary angles:
Any two angles that have a sum of 180°.

The two angles $a°$ and $b°$ are supplementary.

Vertically opposite angles:
Equal angles that are opposite each other when two lines are crossed.

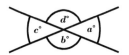

$a° = c°$ and $b° = d°$; i.e. vertically opposite angles are always equal.

Corresponding angles:
The angles which are identical to each other between a transversal and parallel lines.

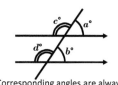

Corresponding angles are always equal; i.e. $a° = b°$ and $c° = d°$.

Angles in a revolution:
The angles formed when lines intersect each other at a point.

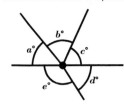

$a° + b° + c° + d° + e° = 360°$; i.e. angles in a revolution always add up to 360°.

2D Shapes

Figures with two dimensions: length and width, but no depth.

Circle:	Right-angled triangle:	Equilateral triangle:	Isosceles triangle:	Scalene triangle:
r = radius *d* = diameter	1 angle is a right angle (90°).	All 3 angles are equal (60°). All 3 sides are of equal length.	2 angles are equal. 2 sides are of equal length.	No angles are equal. No sides are of equal length.

Square:	Trapezium:	Rhombus:	Parallelogram:	Kite:
All 4 angles are equal (90°). All 4 sides are of equal length. The diagonals bisect each other at 90°.	1 pair of opposite sides is parallel.	Opposite angles are equal. All sides are of equal length. The diagonals bisect each other at 90°.	Opposite angles are equal. Opposite sides are parallel. The diagonals bisect each other. Opposite sides are of equal lengths.	2 pairs of sides are of equal lengths. 1 pair of opposite angles is equal. The diagonals intersect at 90°.

Regular pentagon:	Regular hexagon:	Regular heptagon:	Regular octagon:	Regular nonagon:
All 5 angles are equal. All 5 sides are of equal length. The sum of the interior angles is 540°.	All 6 angles are equal. All 6 sides are of equal length. The sum of the interior angles is 720°.	All 7 angles are equal. All 7 sides are of equal length. The sum of the interior angles is 900°.	All 8 angles are equal. All 8 sides are of equal length. The sum of the interior angles is 1080°.	All 9 angles are equal. All 9 sides are of equal length. The sum of the interior angles is 1260°.

3D Shapes

Figures with three dimensions: length, width and height.

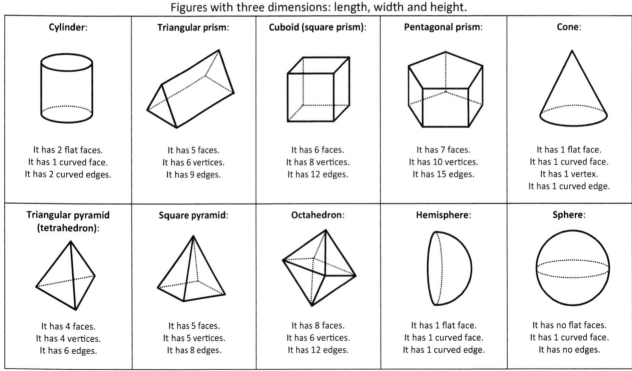

Cylinder:	Triangular prism:	Cuboid (square prism):	Pentagonal prism:	Cone:
It has 2 flat faces. It has 1 curved face. It has 2 curved edges.	It has 5 faces. It has 6 vertices. It has 9 edges.	It has 6 faces. It has 8 vertices. It has 12 edges.	It has 7 faces. It has 10 vertices. It has 15 edges.	It has 1 flat face. It has 1 curved face. It has 1 vertex. It has 1 curved edge.

Triangular pyramid (tetrahedron):	Square pyramid:	Octahedron:	Hemisphere:	Sphere:
It has 4 faces. It has 4 vertices. It has 6 edges.	It has 5 faces. It has 5 vertices. It has 8 edges.	It has 8 faces. It has 6 vertices. It has 12 edges.	It has 1 flat face. It has 1 curved face. It has 1 curved edge.	It has no flat faces. It has 1 curved face. It has no edges.

Area Formulae

Area of a polygon = $\frac{1}{2}$ × apothem × perimeter

= $\frac{1}{2} \times a \times p$

Area of a triangle = $\frac{1}{2}$ × base × perpendicular height

= $\frac{1}{2} \times b \times h$

Area of a circle = pi × radius^2

= $\pi \times r^2$

Area of a parallelogram = base × perpendicular height

= $b \times h$

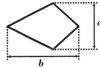

Area of a kite = $\frac{1}{2}$ × product of the two diagonals

= $\frac{1}{2} \times a \times b$

Area of a quadrilateral = length × width

= $l \times w$

Area of a rhombus = $\frac{1}{2}$ × product of the two diagonals

= $\frac{1}{2} \times a \times b$

Area of a trapezium = $\frac{1}{2}$ × sum of the lengths of the parallel sides × perpendicular height

= $\frac{1}{2} \times (a + b) \times h$

Volume Formulae

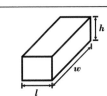

Volume of a cuboid = length × width × height

= $l \times w \times h$

Volume of a prism = area of cross-section × height

= $B \times h$

Other Useful Formulae

Surface area of a 3D shape = sum of the areas of all the faces

Perimeter of a shape = sum of the lengths of all the sides

Circumference of a circle = 2 × pi × radius

= $2 \times \pi \times r$

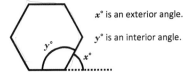

$x°$ is an exterior angle.

$y°$ is an interior angle.

An exterior angle of a regular polygon = $^{360°}/_{\text{number of sides}}$

= $^{360°}/_{n}$

An interior angle of a regular polygon = $^{180° \times (\text{number of sides - 2})}/_{\text{number of sides}}$

= $^{180° \times (n - 2)}/_{n}$

Probability

A measure of how likely it is for an event to occur.
The probability of event A happening is given by: P(A) = number of favourable outcomes ÷ total number of outcomes.

'And' rule:
The 'and' rule is used to find the probability of a combination of independent events.

The probability of events A and B happening is:
P(A and B) = P(A) × P(B)

The word 'and' is replaced by a multiplication sign.

'Or' rule:
The 'or' rule is used to find the probability of a combination of mutually exclusive events.

The probability of event A or B happening is:
P(A or B) = P(A) + P(B)

The word 'or' is replaced by an addition sign.

Tree diagram:
One way of illustrating probability of events is by using branches, e.g. a tree diagram illustrating two tosses of an unbiased coin.

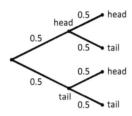

You can use the 'and' rule and 'or' rule with the tree diagram. Simply multiply probability along the branches, and add probabilities down the columns.

Probability scale:
A scale, which goes from zero to one, measuring the likelihood of an outcome.

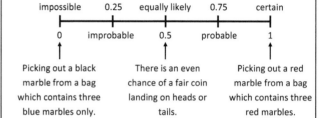

Remember that probabilities can be expressed using fractions, decimals or percentages.

Venn diagram:
A diagram showing all logical relations for a collection of sets using overlapping circles, non-overlapping circles and a rectangular boundary.

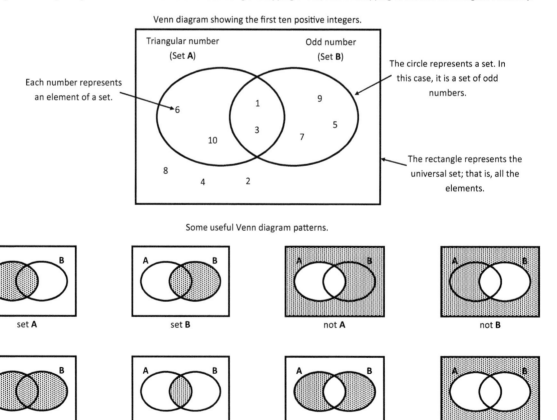

FIRST PAST THE POST®

Numerical Reasoning

Quick Fire Multiple Choice Test 1

Marking Grid

Question	1	2	3	4	5	6	7	8	9	10	11	12	13	14	15	16	17	18	19	20	Total
✓ ✗																					/20

Read the following instructions carefully:

1. You have 6 minutes to complete this test of 20 questions.

2. Work as quickly and as carefully as you can.

3. When you have finished a page, go straight onto the next page until you finish the test.

4. You can use all the available space around the question to do your working; however, answer the question by drawing a circle around one of the options provided.

5. To change an answer, either rub it out or put a fine line across your original answer and circle the new answer.

6. If you cannot answer a question, go on to the next question.

7. When you have completed this paper go back to any questions you have missed out and check your answers.

8. Calculators, rulers and protractors are not permitted in this test.

Good luck!

Test 1

Question 1

Fifty-six children are playing football and rugby during a school sports lesson. If $^5/_8$ of them are playing football, how many are playing rugby?

A	B	C	D	E
21	56	26	32	18

Question 2

What is the value of 3 in the number 4,036?

A	B	C	D	E
300	30	3	0.03	0.3

Question 3

The product of two numbers is 544. If one of the numbers is 32, what is the other number?

A	B	C	D	E
16	21	17	15	19

Question 4

Which one of the 2D shapes labelled A to E below has an order of rotational symmetry of 4?

A   B   C   D   E

Question 5

What are the prime factors of the number 30?

A	B	C	D	E
1, 2, 15	1, 5, 6	1, 5, 30	2, 3, 30	2, 3, 5

Test 1

Question 6

The number machine below has two inputs a and b. If a is 27 and the output is 51, what is b?

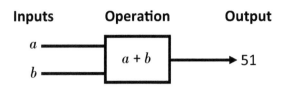

	A	B	C	D	E
	14	28	24	34	26

Question 7

Zak cuts a 2m length of pipe into two pieces in the ratio 3 : 2. What is the length of the longest piece?

A	B	C	D	E
180cm	90cm	100cm	80cm	120cm

Question 8

Fatou wants to multiply the decimal number 17.301468 by a number n to change it into a whole number. Mark the n value below that could achieve Fatou's aim.

A	B	C	D	E
1,000	100,000	1,000,000	10,000	100

Question 9

The pie chart shows the fruits preferred by a group of 80 children. Numbers of children are shown in brackets. What is the angle on the chart associated with oranges?

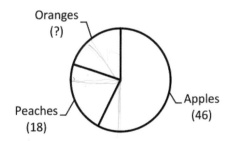

A	B	C	D	E
72°	85°	90°	68°	76°

Question 10

The diagram below shows the coordinates of the left end (A) and centre point (C) of a horizontal line. What are the coordinates of end B?

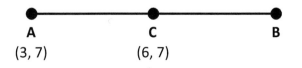

A	B	C	D	E
(10, 7)	(9, 6)	(8, 7)	(6, 7)	(9, 7)

Test 1

Question 11

What is the mode of the set of numbers below if the mean is 4?

1	**7**	**2**	**?**	**3**

A	B	C	D	E
7	2	3	1	5

Question 12

What is the combined volume of the two identical 3D wedge shapes shown below?

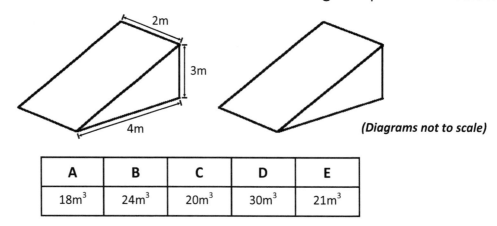

2m

3m

4m

(Diagrams not to scale)

A	B	C	D	E
18m^3	24m^3	20m^3	30m^3	21m^3

Question 13

What is the perimeter of the shaded shape below if x represents a length of 10cm?

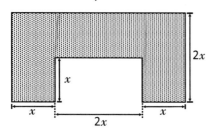

A	B	C	D	E
135cm	140cm	145cm	120cm	125cm

Question 14

What is angle $t°$ in the shape below?

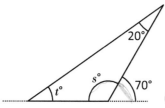

(Diagram not to scale)

A	B	C	D	E
41°	39°	45°	50°	52°

Question 15

Amit adds the 3rd square number to the 3rd cube number and then square roots the result. What should his answer be?

A	B	C	D	E
4	9	6	7	5

Question 16

Pippa selects two numbers at random, one from the set of numbers 1, 3, 5, and one from the set of numbers 2, 4, 6. What is the probability that the sum of the two numbers is greater than 8? Express your answer as a fraction in its lowest terms.

A	B	C	D	E
$\frac{1}{3}$	$\frac{1}{4}$	$\frac{1}{6}$	$\frac{2}{3}$	$\frac{1}{2}$

Question 17

Which of the 3D shapes A to E below has more faces than vertices?

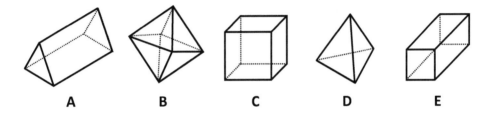

| A | B | C | D | E |

Question 18

What is 214 minutes expressed in hours and minutes?

A	B	C	D	E
3hr 24min	2hr 14min	3hr 4min	4hr	3hr 34min

Question 19

A map is drawn to a scale of 1 : 500. How many metres would be represented by 8cm on the map?

A	B	C	D	E
40m	54cm	38m	400m	50m

Question 20

What is the missing number in the sequence below?

| ? | 6 | 12 | 24 | 48 |

A	B	C	D	E
6	4	3	2	1

BLANK PAGE

FIRST PAST THE POST®

Numerical Reasoning

Quick Fire Multiple Choice Test 2

Marking Grid																					
Question	1	2	3	4	5	6	7	8	9	10	11	12	13	14	15	16	17	18	19	20	Total
✓ ✗																					/20

Read the following instructions carefully:

1. You have 6 minutes to complete this test of 20 questions.

2. Work as quickly and as carefully as you can.

3. When you have finished a page, go straight onto the next page until you finish the test.

4. You can use all the available space around the question to do your working; however, answer the question by drawing a circle around one of the options provided.

5. To change an answer, either rub it out or put a fine line across your original answer and circle the new answer.

6. If you cannot answer a question, go on to the next question.

7. When you have completed this paper go back to any questions you have missed out and check your answers.

8. Calculators, rulers and protractors are not permitted in this test.

Good luck!

Once you have completed each test and marked it using the answers at the back you can anonymously go online and compare your child's performance relative to peers who have completed the same test(s) using our 11+ Peer Compare System™. Register at http://peercompare.elevenplusexams.co.uk/ and then activate the access code printed on the front inside cover of this book.

Test 2

Question 1

The lengths of three nails A, B and C are shown on the ruler below. What is the result of 2 × (A + B + C)?

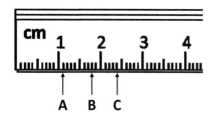

A	B	C	D	E
9.5cm	11cm	10.6cm	9.8cm	10.4cm

Question 2

Krishna has saved £63 towards his target of £70. What percentage of the total is this?

A	B	C	D	E
90%	85%	92%	70%	89.3%

Question 3

A   H   J   N   O   T   X   Z

How many of the letters above have at least one line of symmetry?

A	B	C	D	E
7	1	3	6	5

Question 4

What is the answer to the Roman numeral sum XVI + XIV?

A	B	C	D	E
XXXI	XXV	XXX	XX	VXXX

Question 5

The volume of a cuboid is 10 inches^3. Its length (l) and width (w) are 5 inches and 1 inch respectively. Using the conversion 1 inch = 2.54cm, what is the height (h) of the cuboid expressed in centimetres (cm)?

A	B	C	D	E
2.54cm	4.98cm	5cm	5.1cm	5.08cm

Test 2

Question 6

Round 0.0816 to 3 decimal places.

A	B	C	D	E
0.082	0.816	0.081	0.090	0.100

Question 7

If $2r + 56 = 10r$, what is the value of r?

A	B	C	D	E
9	8	6	10	7

Question 8

What is the output of the number machine below?

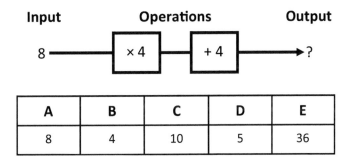

A	B	C	D	E
8	4	10	5	36

Question 9

Mr Clement left Poole Harbour in his yacht at 12:52 and sailed out to sea. 2,700 seconds later he returned to the harbour. At what time did Mr Clement return? Give your answer in 24-hour clock format.

A	B	C	D	E
13:40	13:37	14:12	13:00	13:28

Question 10

Look at the five sets of temperatures T1 to T5 below. Which set has the greatest range?

T1 (°C)	1	-5	-3	-2	0	-1	3
T2 (°C)	0	2	0	-3	1	-2	3
T3 (°C)	3	4	-3	2	2	-5	0
T4 (°C)	2	3	1	-2	0	3	2
T5 (°C)	1	7	4	3	2	5	0

A	B	C	D	E
T1	T2	T3	T4	T5

Test 2

Question 11

Which of the fractions shown is equivalent to $^2/_9$?

A	B	C	D	E
$^{16}/_{81}$	$^1/_3$	$^4/_{20}$	$^{18}/_{81}$	$^{15}/_{73}$

Question 12

The ratio of teas (t) to coffees (c) made in a household over a two day period is 3 : 1. How many of each drink is made if the combined number of drinks is 24?

A	B	C	D	E
$t = 10$, $c = 3$	$t = 14$, $c = 10$	$t = 18$, $c = 6$	$t = 9$, $c = 15$	$t = 20$, $c = 4$

Question 13

How many thousands equal 70 hundreds?

A	B	C	D	E
10	7	0.7	70	1.7

Question 14

The pie chart below shows the population sizes of four insect types. If the total number of insects is one thousand, what percentage of the population are cockroaches?

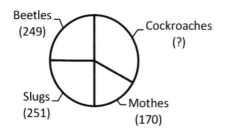

Beetles (249)
Cockroaches (?)
Slugs (251)
Mothes (170)

A	B	C	D	E
330%	40%	44%	100%	33%

Question 15

How many pairs of parallel sides does a rhombus and trapezium have in total?

A	B	C	D	E
4	2	1	8	3

Test 2

Question 16

Point Q has coordinates (-5, 0). What are the new coordinates of point Q when it is rotated 90˚ anticlockwise about the origin (0, 0)?

A	B	C	D	E
(0, 5)	(-5, 0)	(0, -5)	(5, -5)	(-5, 5)

Question 17

The side length x on the rectangle below is 3cm. What is the distance around the outside of the shape?

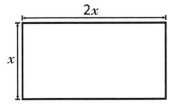

(Diagram not to scale)

A	B	C	D	E
6cm	8cm	1.8m	18cm	800mm

Question 18

A can of lemonade holds 330ml. How many litres of lemonade are there in 7 cans?

A	B	C	D	E
2.31L	3,300ml	2.1L	3.3L	231L

Question 19

Julie has 14 balls numbered 1 to 14 in a bag. What is the probability that Julie can take out a ball at random with a number greater than 10 on it? Express your answer as a fraction in its lowest terms.

A	B	C	D	E
$^4/_7$	$^2/_{14}$	$^2/_7$	$^1/_6$	$^1/_3$

Question 20

What is the product of 24 and 36?

A	B	C	D	E
824	864	818	624	700

BLANK PAGE

Numerical Reasoning

Quick Fire Multiple Choice Test 3

Marking Grid																					
Question	1	2	3	4	5	6	7	8	9	10	11	12	13	14	15	16	17	18	19	20	Total
✓ ✗																					/20

Read the following instructions carefully:

1. You have 6 minutes to complete this test of 20 questions.

2. Work as quickly and as carefully as you can.

3. When you have finished a page, go straight onto the next page until you finish the test.

4. You can use all the available space around the question to do your working; however, answer the question by drawing a circle around one of the options provided.

5. To change an answer, either rub it out or put a fine line across your original answer and circle the new answer.

6. If you cannot answer a question, go on to the next question.

7. When you have completed this paper go back to any questions you have missed out and check your answers.

8. Calculators, rulers and protractors are not permitted in this test.

Good luck!

Once you have completed each test and marked it using the answers at the back you can anonymously go online and compare your child's performance relative to peers who have completed the same test(s) using our 11+ Peer Compare System™. Register at http://peercompare.elevenplusexams.co.uk/ and then activate the access code printed on the front inside cover of this book.

Test 3

Question 1

What is the value of the 7 in the number 27,104?

A	B	C	D	E
700	7	0.7	7,000	70

Question 2

What are the numbers x and y that belong in the flow chart below?

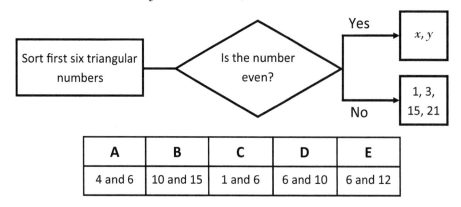

A	B	C	D	E
4 and 6	10 and 15	1 and 6	6 and 10	6 and 12

Question 3

What is 0.47 litres expressed in millilitres (ml)?

A	B	C	D	E
470ml	47ml	4.7ml	4,700ml	0.47ml

Question 4

Adele spent £4 on ten pencils, each costing 17p, and one pen. How much did Adele pay for the pen?

A	B	C	D	E
£2.78	£2.30	£0.78	£3.00	£2.54

Question 5

The fair die below is thrown. What is the probability of rolling a prime number?

A	B	C	D	E
$\frac{1}{2}$	$\frac{1}{3}$	1	$\frac{1}{4}$	$\frac{1}{6}$

Test 3

Question 6

What is the missing term in the sequence below?

0.5   1.5   ?   13.5   40.5

A	B	C	D	E
10.5	5.5	5	4.5	6.5

Question 7

Look at the number machine below. What is the output?

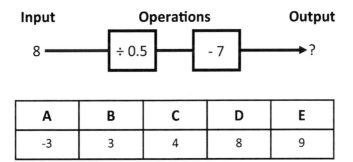

A	B	C	D	E
-3	3	4	8	9

Question 8

What is the value of z in the expression $2(x + 4y) = 9z$ if $x = 6$ and $y = 3$?

A	B	C	D	E
4	18	6	2	12

Question 9

A rectangle has the following corner coordinates: (0, 0), (0, 2), (8, 2), (8, 0).
What are the coordinates at the mid-point of the rectangle?

A	B	C	D	E
(4, 1)	(8, 1)	(4, 2)	(0, 1)	(4, 0)

Question 10

The arrow on the number line below is pointing to a value of 12. What is the value on the scale at P?

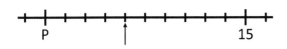

A	B	C	D	E
9	11	10	9.5	10.5

Test 3

Question 11

If the pair of ratios 3 : 7 and 24 : n are equivalent, what is the value of n?

A	B	C	D	E
56	21	34	8	78

Question 12

Pierre's journey by car started at 10am and is shown on the line graph below.
He stopped off at a motorway service station for a break during his trip. What time did Pierre leave the motorway services?

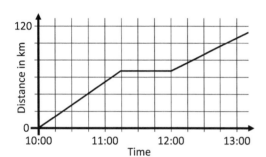

A	B	C	D	E
10:00	13:00	11:00	12:00	13:40

Question 13

A cube has a side length of 3cm. What is the volume of a cuboid created by two such cubes placed side by side?

A	B	C	D	E
13.5cm^3	27cm^2	18cm^3	27cm^3	54cm^3

Question 14

Point P, at coordinates (0, -9), is rotated 90° anticlockwise about (0, 0). What are the new coordinates of P?

A	B	C	D	E
(0, 9)	(9, 0)	(0, 0)	(-9, 0)	(9, -9)

Question 15

How many vertices in total are on the three shapes below?

 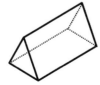

A	B	C	D	E
27	14	17	9	18

Test 3

Question 16

What is the mean of the set of numbers below?

5   1   6   5   3   4

A	B	C	D	E
4.5	6	3.5	5	4

Question 17

Look at the isosceles triangle below. What is angle $a°$?

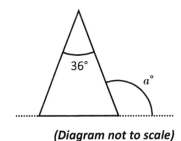

(Diagram not to scale)

A	B	C	D	E
134°	120°	108°	144°	72°

Question 18

Sixteen of the forty counters in a box are red. What percentage are not red?

A	B	C	D	E
80%	64%	36%	40%	60%

Question 19

The perimeter of a rectangle is 42cm and its length is twice its width. Find the width.

A	B	C	D	E
7cm	8cm	12cm	16cm	10cm

Question 20

Which one of the following five properties do the following three 2D shapes have in common: isosceles triangle, kite and isosceles trapezium?

A	B	C	D	E
One 90° angle	Order of rotational symmetry is 2	One pair of parallel lines	One line of symmetry	Number of sides is 3

BLANK PAGE

FIRST PAST THE POST®

Numerical Reasoning

Quick Fire Multiple Choice Test 4

Marking Grid																					
Question	1	2	3	4	5	6	7	8	9	10	11	12	13	14	15	16	17	18	19	20	Total
✓ ✗																					/20

Read the following instructions carefully:

1. You have 6 minutes to complete this test of 20 questions.

2. Work as quickly and as carefully as you can.

3. When you have finished a page, go straight onto the next page until you finish the test.

4. You can use all the available space around the question to do your working; however, answer the question by drawing a circle around one of the options provided.

5. To change an answer, either rub it out or put a fine line across your original answer and circle the new answer.

6. If you cannot answer a question, go on to the next question.

7. When you have completed this paper go back to any questions you have missed out and check your answers.

8. Calculators, rulers and protractors are not permitted in this test.

Good luck!

Once you have completed each test and marked it using the answers at the back you can anonymously go online and compare your child's performance relative to peers who have completed the same test(s) using our 11+ Peer Compare System™. Register at http://peercompare.elevenplusexams.co.uk/ and then activate the access code printed on the front inside cover of this book.

Test 4

Question 1

Rahul multiplies the number 480 by 11 and then divides the answer by 6. What should be Rahul's final result?

A	B	C	D	E
880	580	680	980	780

Question 2

Three-quarters of Ruth's savings is £12.00. How much has Ruth saved altogether?

A	B	C	D	E
£9	£16	£20	£18	£15

Question 3

The output of the number machine below is 50. What is the input n?

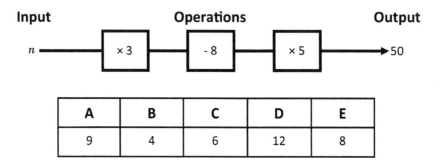

A	B	C	D	E
9	4	6	12	8

Question 4

Look at the price of electrical goods below. How much more does it cost to buy the computer and camera separately than to buy them as a combined package?

Computer £380   Camera £70

Combined computer & camera £435

A	B	C	D	E
£10	£15	£5	£20	£25

Question 5

What is 'thirty-seven thousand and twenty' expressed in number format?

A	B	C	D	E
3,720	30,702	37,020	37,200	37,000,020

Test 4

Question 6

What are the factors of 18?

A	B	C	D	E
2, 3, 6, 9	1, 2, 4, 8, 9, 36	1, 2, 3, 6, 9, 18	2, 6, 9, 18	1, 3, 6, 9, 18

Question 7

Alison thinks of a number x and trebles it. She then subtracts 17 and gets a final result of 25. What is the number x Alison started with?

A	B	C	D	E
14	16	17	25	13

Question 8

How many degrees below 7°C is - 24°C?

A	B	C	D	E
17	31	32	18	33

Question 9

The numbers in the grid below follow a pattern. What is the missing number?

11	18	25
18	25	32
25	32	?

A	B	C	D	E
32	33	11	18	39

Question 10

What is 0.64 expressed as a fraction in its lowest terms? Mark your answer below.

A	B	C	D	E
$\frac{8}{13}$	$\frac{32}{50}$	$\frac{7}{5}$	$\frac{16}{25}$	$\frac{8}{50}$

Test 4

Question 11

The number of bicycles passing a traffic survey checkpoint every hour is shown on the bar chart below. How many bicycles passed by at 09:00?

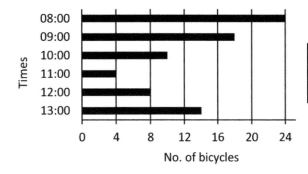

A	B	C	D	E
16	17	18	19	20

Question 12

A common three-sided 2D shape has sides of different lengths and no equal angles. Mark the name of the shape below.

A	B	C	D	E
Isosceles triangle	Rhombus	Scalene triangle	Kite	Equilateral triangle

Question 13

What is the value of angle $a°$ in the parallelogram below?

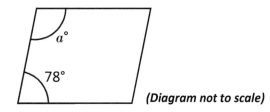

(Diagram not to scale)

A	B	C	D	E
78°	79°	80°	87°	102°

Question 14

A box contains five balls numbered 1 to 5. What is the probability of randomly selecting a ball which has an odd number on it?

A	B	C	D	E
$\frac{1}{3}$	$\frac{4}{5}$	$\frac{1}{2}$	$\frac{3}{5}$	$\frac{1}{5}$

Question 15

In a class of 27 children there are 5 boys to every 4 girls. How many boys are in the class?

A	B	C	D	E
5	10	15	12	20

Question 16

If the horizontal and vertical distances between any two dots on the grid below is 2cm, what is the area of the triangle?

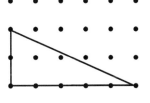

A	B	C	D	E
5cm^2	40cm^2	20cm^2	10cm^2	22cm^2

(Diagram not to scale)

Question 17

How many edges does an octagonal prism have?

A	B	C	D	E
16	28	24	20	32

Question 18

A straight line AB has end coordinates A(3, 2) and B(3, 9). Which one of the following coordinates are on the same line?

A	B	C	D	E
(2, 3)	(4, 5)	(3, 8)	(7, 3)	(3, 1)

Question 19

John sums the order of rotational symmetry of an equilateral triangle and the number of lines of symmetry of a rhombus. What should John's final answer be?

A	B	C	D	E
1	2	3	4	5

Question 20

What is the time three-quarters of an hour before 2.25 pm expressed in 24-hour clock notation?

A	B	C	D	E
13:40	13:45	13:35	14:05	14:00

BLANK PAGE

FIRST PAST THE POST®

Numerical Reasoning

Quick Fire Multiple Choice Test 5

Marking Grid																					
Question	1	2	3	4	5	6	7	8	9	10	11	12	13	14	15	16	17	18	19	20	Total
✓ ✗																					/20

Read the following instructions carefully:

1. You have 6 minutes to complete this test of 20 questions.

2. Work as quickly and as carefully as you can.

3. When you have finished a page, go straight onto the next page until you finish the test.

4. You can use all the available space around the question to do your working; however, answer the question by drawing a circle around one of the options provided.

5. To change an answer, either rub it out or put a fine line across your original answer and circle the new answer.

6. If you cannot answer a question, go on to the next question.

7. When you have completed this paper go back to any questions you have missed out and check your answers.

8. Calculators, rulers and protractors are not permitted in this test.

Good luck!

Once you have completed each test and marked it using the answers at the back you can anonymously go online and compare your child's performance relative to peers who have completed the same test(s) using our 11+ Peer Compare System™. Register at http://peercompare.elevenplusexams.co.uk/ and then activate the access code printed on the front inside cover of this book.

Test 5

Question 1

What is $^{53}/_8$ expressed as a mixed number?

A	B	C	D	E
$6\,^5/_8$	$6\,^5/_5$	$5\,^{13}/_8$	$6\,^3/_4$	$8\,^5/_8$

Question 2

Connor writes down 3.68 to the nearest tenth. What should Connor's answer be?

A	B	C	D	E
3.7	3.6	3.78	3.57	3.65

Question 3

How many 18p pencils can be bought with £2.52?

A	B	C	D	E
14	18	15	16	17

Question 4

Look at the shape and mirror line M at the left of the diagrams below. Which one of the options A to E shows the mirror image?

A	B	C	D	E

Question 5

What is the smallest number that is a common multiple of 2, 4 and 6?

A	B	C	D	E
6	10	28	16	12

Test 5

Question 6

What number should replace the question mark in Operation 1 of the function machine shown below?

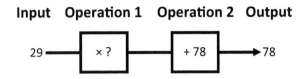

A	B	C	D	E
0	1	2	3	4

Question 7

Two islands P and Q have a population ratio of 7 : 2 respectively. If the total population of the two islands is 1836, how many people live on island Q?

A	B	C	D	E
408	452	500	412	440

Question 8

What is the second largest of the following five decimal numbers?

A	B	C	D	E
6.666	6.06	6.60	6.606	6.006

Question 9

Which number belongs in the overlapping area of the Venn diagram?

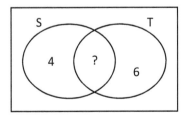

A	B	C	D	E
49	16	36	100	21

S = square numbers

T = triangular numbers

Question 10

Point P, at (-3, 2), is reflected in the y-axis. What are the coordinates of the reflected image of point P?

A	B	C	D	E
(-3, -2)	(3, 2)	(-3, 2)	(3, -2)	(2, -3)

Test 5

Question 11

What is the median of the set of numbers below?

2	5	1	8	4	3	5

A	B	C	D	E
5	4	1	3	2

Question 12

If the triangular prism below has an end area of 9.4cm^2, what is its volume?

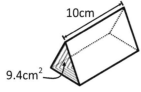

10cm

9.4cm^2

(Diagram not to scale)

A	B	C	D	E
94cm^2	0.94m	9.4m^3	94cm^3	940cm^3

Question 13

The cost of a pencil is x pence and the cost of a pen is 9 pence more than a pencil. What is the total cost in pence of a pencil and 3 pens?

A	B	C	D	E
$6 + 6x$	$2x + 2$	$3x + 18$	$x + 6$	$4x + 27$

Question 14

Which one of the lines N, P, R, S, T is perpendicular to line Q?

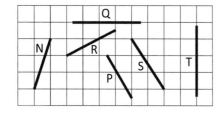

A	B	C	D	E
N	T	R	P	S

Question 15

MMXII is a year expressed in Roman numerals. What is this year in normal whole number format?

A	B	C	D	E
2008	1020	2012	2021	2011

Test 5

Question 16

What is the probability of **not** getting a 2 or a 4 when a six-sided fair dice numbered 1 to 6 is rolled?

A	B	C	D	E
$^1/_2$	$^1/_6$	$^1/_3$	$^5/_6$	$^2/_3$

Question 17

Which **two** of the nets 1 to 5 below create 3D pyramids when folded?

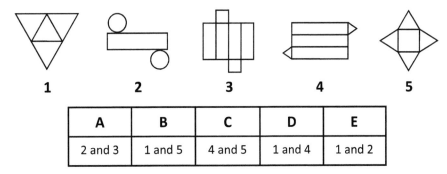

1	2	3	4	5

A	B	C	D	E
2 and 3	1 and 5	4 and 5	1 and 4	1 and 2

Question 18

Clover was on holiday from the 26th June to the 7th July. For how many days, including both dates mentioned, was Clover on holiday?

A	B	C	D	E
12	11	13	14	10

Question 19

What is the reading on the scale shown below?

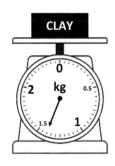

A	B	C	D	E
1.5kg	120g	1.2kg	1.45kg	1.4kg

Question 20

What is the common difference between terms in the number sequence below?

1.25   1.30   1.35   1.40   1.45   1.50

A	B	C	D	E
1.05	5	1.5	0.5	0.05

BLANK PAGE

FIRST PAST THE POST®

Numerical Reasoning

Quick Fire Multiple Choice Test 6

Marking Grid																					
Question	1	2	3	4	5	6	7	8	9	10	11	12	13	14	15	16	17	18	19	20	Total
✓ ✗																					/20

Read the following instructions carefully:

1. You have 6 minutes to complete this test of 20 questions.

2. Work as quickly and as carefully as you can.

3. When you have finished a page, go straight onto the next page until you finish the test.

4. You can use all the available space around the question to do your working; however, answer the question by drawing a circle around one of the options provided.

5. To change an answer, either rub it out or put a fine line across your original answer and circle the new answer.

6. If you cannot answer a question, go on to the next question.

7. When you have completed this paper go back to any questions you have missed out and check your answers.

8. Calculators, rulers and protractors are not permitted in this test.

Good luck!

Test 6

Question 1

What is the area of the rectangle shown below?

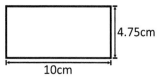

4.75cm

10cm

(Diagram not to scale)

A	B	C	D	E
4.75cm^3	0.475m^2	47.5cm^2	47cm^3	475cm^2

Question 2

Express $^{53}/_6$ as a mixed number.

A	B	C	D	E
$8\,^5/_3$	$8\,^5/_6$	$9\,^1/_6$	$8\,^1/_3$	$7\,^7/_6$

Question 3

What is the total number of edges on 2 heptagons and 1 octagon?

A	B	C	D	E
8	14	24	10	22

Question 4

What is the value of x in the equation below?

$$21 + x = 45 - x$$

A	B	C	D	E
2	24	66	33	12

Question 5

Matt is facing SW and turns 90° clockwise. In which direction is Matt now facing?

A	B	C	D	E
N	NW	NE	WSW	S

Test 6

Question 6

Find the median of the set of numbers below.

6   5   7   2   11   8   1   7

A	B	C	D	E
7	6	5.875	5.5	6.5

Question 7

The ratio of boys to girls in a class of 63 children is 4 : 5. How many boys are in the class?

A	B	C	D	E
20	28	7	35	9

Question 8

What is the input of the number machine below?

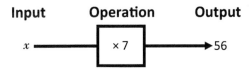

A	B	C	D	E
7	9	10	7.5	8

Question 9

Using only the positive square root of 49, what is $3 \times (8 - 3) + \sqrt{49} - 3^2$?

A	B	C	D	E
15	17	-2	13	10

Question 10

What is the height ($h$cm) of the cuboid below if its volume is 60cm^3?

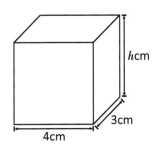

(Diagram not to scale)

A	B	C	D	E
20cm	4cm^2	20cm	5cm	12cm

Test 6

Question 11

How many edges does a triangular pyramid have?

A	B	C	D	E
2	3	4	5	6

Question 12

Convert 647mm into centimetres (cm).

A	B	C	D	E
6.47cm	0.647cm	647cm	67.4cm	64.7cm

Question 13

What is the reading on the scale below?

A	B	C	D	E
1.85kg	1.90kg	1.7kg	1.8kg	1.75kg

Question 14

What is the value of the 8 in the number 42.86?

A	B	C	D	E
80	8	$^8/_{10}$	$^8/_{100}$	$^4/_{25}$

Question 15

The pie chart gives the number of students who walk to school. How many students travel to school by bus?

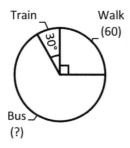

A	B	C	D	E
160	90	270	240	180

Test 6

Question 16

Express 4.28pm in 24-hour clock format.

A	B	C	D	E
14:28	04:28	12:28	08:28	16:28

Question 17

In its simplest form, what is the probability of scoring a square number when the fair die below is rolled?

A	B	C	D	E
$^1/_6$	$^1/_3$	$^2/_3$	$^1/_4$	$^5/_6$

Question 18

The top corners of a square with 6cm sides have coordinates (3, 7) and (9, 7). What are the coordinates of the centre of the square?

A	B	C	D	E
(4, 6)	(-6, 4)	(6, -4)	(6, 4)	(9, 4)

Question 19

What is the order of rotational symmetry of a regular decagon about its centre?

A	B	C	D	E
4	10	8	6	12

Question 20

What percentage of the squares on the shape below are shaded?

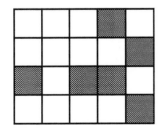

A	B	C	D	E
30%	45%	25%	40%	38%

BLANK PAGE

FIRST PAST THE POST®

Numerical Reasoning

Quick Fire Multiple Choice Test 7

Marking Grid																					
Question	1	2	3	4	5	6	7	8	9	10	11	12	13	14	15	16	17	18	19	20	Total
✓ ✗																					/20

Read the following instructions carefully:

1. You have 6 minutes to complete this test of 20 questions.

2. Work as quickly and as carefully as you can.

3. When you have finished a page, go straight onto the next page until you finish the test.

4. You can use all the available space around the question to do your working; however, answer the question by drawing a circle around one of the options provided.

5. To change an answer, either rub it out or put a fine line across your original answer and circle the new answer.

6. If you cannot answer a question, go on to the next question.

7. When you have completed this paper go back to any questions you have missed out and check your answers.

8. Calculators, rulers and protractors are not permitted in this test.

Good luck!

Test 7

Question 1

What is the number 5,358 rounded to the nearest hundred?

A	B	C	D	E
5,400	5,300	5,350	5,360	5,000

Question 2

What is the perimeter of the rectangle shown below?

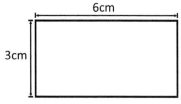

3cm

6cm

(Diagram not to scale)

A	B	C	D	E
18cm^2	9cm	18cm	9cm^2	12cm^2

Question 3

A triangle has two 70° interior angles. What is the third interior angle?

A	B	C	D	E
180°	90°	70°	40°	50°

Question 4

Find the input to the number machine below.

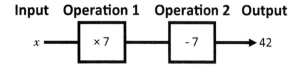

A	B	C	D	E
49	7	40	42	47

Question 5

What is the sum of the number of faces, edges and vertices of a triangular pyramid?

A	B	C	D	E
14	20	13	12	15

Test 7

Question 6

What is the probability of scoring a cube number on the fair spinner shown below?

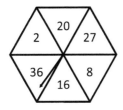

A	B	C	D	E
$\frac{1}{6}$	$\frac{1}{3}$	$\frac{1}{2}$	$\frac{2}{3}$	$\frac{1}{4}$

Question 7

Write down the result of (354 ÷ 6.3) × 0.

A	B	C	D	E
0	56.19	348	347.7	354

Question 8

What are the coordinates of corner C of the parallelogram below?

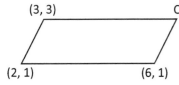

(Diagram not to scale)

A	B	C	D	E
(2, 3)	(2, 1)	(6, 3)	(3, 7)	(7, 3)

Question 9

What is the volume of a cube with a width of 10cm?

A	B	C	D	E
100cm³	10cm³	1,000cm³	1,000cm²	10cm²

Question 10

In the diagram below, the number in a circle is the sum of the numbers in the two circles just beneath it. What is the number in the top box?

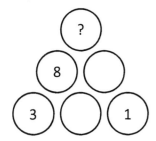

A	B	C	D	E
10	12	11	14	15

Test 7

Question 11

Express $6 \frac{1}{5}$ in decimal number format.

A	B	C	D	E
6.1	6.15	6.9	6.2	6.5

Question 12

How many children own a cat according to the results displayed by the Venn diagram below?

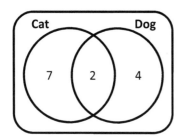

A	B	C	D	E
7	2	9	4	11

Question 13

What is the missing number in the sequence below?

22	21	19	16	?	7	1

A	B	C	D	E
15	12	11	14	8

Question 14

Hanna catches a bus at 10.45am. The journey takes 23 minutes. At what time does Hanna reach her destination? Express your answer in 24-hour clock format.

A	B	C	D	E
10.49am	23:05	11:08	11:23	23:08

Question 15

What percentage of the numbers below are prime?

4   7   9   23   27

A	B	C	D	E
10%	40%	20%	60%	100%

Test 7

Question 16

Which of the following is an equivalent ratio to 24 : 36?

A	B	C	D	E
1 : 3	2 : 3	1 : 4	2 : 5	18 : 38

Question 17

Point P has coordinates (-3, 4). If P is translated 5 units right and 4 units down, what are its new coordinates?

A	B	C	D	E
(2, 0)	(-8, 0)	(-8, 8)	(2, 8)	(0, 2)

Question 18

How much water, expressed in millilitres (ml), is in the jug shown below?

A	B	C	D	E
150ml	450ml	1500ml	300ml	100ml

Question 19

What is the reading at point B on the ruler shown below? Express your answer in millimetres (mm).

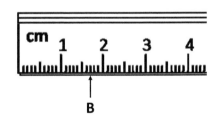

A	B	C	D	E
1.7mm	170mm	177mm	1.77mm	17mm

Question 20

If $3(x + 7) = 63$, what is the value of x?

A	B	C	D	E
53	63	28	14	7

BLANK PAGE

FIRST PAST THE POST®

Numerical Reasoning

Quick Fire Multiple Choice Test 8

Marking Grid																					
Question	1	2	3	4	5	6	7	8	9	10	11	12	13	14	15	16	17	18	19	20	Total
✓ ✗																					/20

Read the following instructions carefully:

1. You have 6 minutes to complete this test of 20 questions.

2. Work as quickly and as carefully as you can.

3. When you have finished a page, go straight onto the next page until you finish the test.

4. You can use all the available space around the question to do your working; however, answer the question by drawing a circle around one of the options provided.

5. To change an answer, either rub it out or put a fine line across your original answer and circle the new answer.

6. If you cannot answer a question, go on to the next question.

7. When you have completed this paper go back to any questions you have missed out and check your answers.

8. Calculators, rulers and protractors are not permitted in this test.

Good luck!

Test 8

Question 1

What is the positive square root of $(3^2 + 3^3)$?

A	B	C	D	E
9	36	27	6	18

Question 2

Three corners of a rectangle have coordinates of (5, 2), (5, 6) and (12, 2).

What is the area of the rectangle in square units?

A	B	C	D	E
26 units^2	28 units^2	21 units^2	14 units^3	24 units^2

Question 3

Which of the lines labelled B to G below is perpendicular to line A?

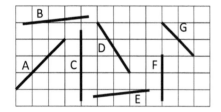

A	B	C	D	E
D	E	F	C	G

Question 4

Farida has 8 red counters and 12 blue counters. In its simplest form, what is the ratio of red to blue counters?

A	B	C	D	E
2 : 3	3 : 2	4 : 7	4 : 6	12 : 8

Question 5

What is the total number of vertices on the three 3D shapes shown below?

Square
pyramid

Cube

Pentagonal
prism

A	B	C	D	E
35	23	20	13	28

Test 8

Question 6

What is the product of 0.1, 0.1 and 1,000?

A	B	C	D	E
100	1	10	0.01	0.1

Question 7

What is input x in the number machine below?

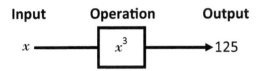

	A	B	C	D	E
	25	81	10	5	15

Question 8

Convert 12,000mg into kilograms (kg).

A	B	C	D	E
120kg	12kg	1.2kg	0.12kg	0.012kg

Question 9

Connor goes on holiday on Saturday 27th June and returns the following month on the 8th. On what day of the week does Connor return?

A	B	C	D	E
Monday	Tuesday	Wednesday	Thursday	Friday

Question 10

What is the probability of selecting an ace or a King at random from a standard set of 52 playing cards? Express your answer as a fraction in its lowest terms.

A	B	C	D	E
$\frac{2}{13}$	$\frac{4}{26}$	$\frac{1}{13}$	$\frac{7}{52}$	$\frac{4}{13}$

Test 8

Question 11

The temperature in London is 1.4°C. If the temperature falls by a further 3.7°C, what is the new temperature?

A	B	C	D	E
2.3°C	5.1°C	-5.1°C	3.1°C	-2.3°C

Question 12

How many of the small 20cm wide cubes can fit inside the box shown below?

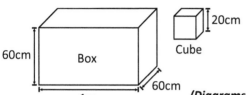

(Diagrams not to scale)

A	B	C	D	E
33	15	50	45	40

Question 13

A right angle triangle has two equal length sides. Write down one of the two smallest interior angles.

A	B	C	D	E
30°	35°	45°	60°	90°

Question 14

Bread costs £1.05 a loaf and milk is 49p a pint. How much will it cost to buy 1 loaf of bread and 2 pints of milk?

A	B	C	D	E
£2.03	£1.54	£2.59	£2.99	£1.20

Question 15

The graph shows how far a car has travelled over time in heavy traffic. What is its speed of travel in kilometres per hour?

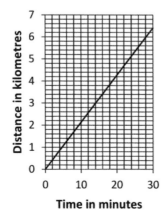

A	B	C	D	E
12.8km per hour	14.2km per hour	10.6km per hour	9.8km per hour	15km per hour

Test 8

Question 16

One side of a regular pentagon is 3cm and one side of a regular nonagon measures 4cm. What is the sum of their combined perimeters?

A	B	C	D	E
15cm	36cm	16cm	51cm	41cm

Question 17

What is the lowest common multiple (LCM) of 20 and 32?

A	B	C	D	E
160	80	240	640	320

Question 18

Pierre is x years old. His mother is 3 times his age, and his father is 4 years older than his mother. What is the age of Pierre's father in terms of x.

A	B	C	D	E
$3x - 4$	$3(x + 4)$	$4(x + 3)$	$4x + 3$	$3x + 4$

Question 19

What is the highest common factor (HCF) of 24 and 32?

A	B	C	D	E
4	8	2	24	12

Question 20

Circles have been used to create the first four shapes in the pattern below. How many circles are needed to create the 7th shape in the pattern?

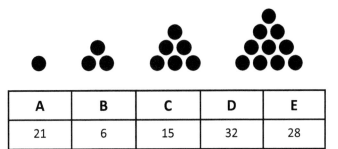

A	B	C	D	E
21	6	15	32	28

BLANK PAGE

FIRST PAST THE POST®

Numerical Reasoning

Quick Fire Multiple Choice Test 9

										Marking Grid											
Question	1	2	3	4	5	6	7	8	9	10	11	12	13	14	15	16	17	18	19	20	Total
✓ ✗																					/20

Read the following instructions carefully:

1. You have 6 minutes to complete this test of 20 questions.

2. Work as quickly and as carefully as you can.

3. When you have finished a page, go straight onto the next page until you finish the test.

4. You can use all the available space around the question to do your working; however, answer the question by drawing a circle around one of the options provided.

5. To change an answer, either rub it out or put a fine line across your original answer and circle the new answer.

6. If you cannot answer a question, go on to the next question.

7. When you have completed this paper go back to any questions you have missed out and check your answers.

8. Calculators, rulers and protractors are not permitted in this test.

Good luck!

Test 9

Question 1

What is the next prime number after 19?

A	B	C	D	E
29	31	27	21	23

Question 2

In its simplest terms, what fraction of circles in the pattern below are shaded?

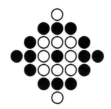

A	B	C	D	E
$\frac{4}{5}$	$\frac{11}{25}$	$\frac{3}{5}$	$\frac{7}{10}$	$\frac{7}{15}$

Question 3

What cube number lies between 30 and 120?

A	B	C	D	E
64	33	100	125	90

Question 4

What is the volume of the wedge shape shown below?

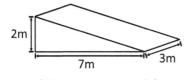

2m
7m
3m

(Diagram not to scale)

A	B	C	D	E
42m³	14m³	27m²	15m²	21m³

Question 5

Kim adds the number of faces to the number of vertices of a hexagonal prism. She then subtracts the number of edges from the result. What answer should Kim get?

A	B	C	D	E
28	38	22	2	4

Test 9

Question 6

What is the total area of the shaded sections in the diagram shown below?

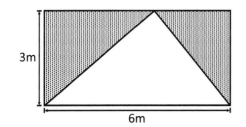

3m

6m

(Diagram not to scale)

A	B	C	D	E
$18m^3$	$18m^2$	$9m^2$	$11m^2$	$10m$

Question 7

Point A has coordinates (0, 6). If point A is rotated 90 clockwise about the origin (0, 0), what are its new coordinates?

A	B	C	D	E
(6, 6)	(6, 0)	(0, -6)	(-6, 6)	(-6, 0)

Question 8

Work out the mean of the set of numbers below.

3   2   5   4   4   1   2

A	B	C	D	E
2.5	3.5	4	3	2

Question 9

If $x = 0.2$, what is the output of the number machine shown below?

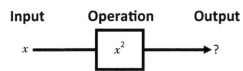

Input   Operation   Output

x ———— x^2 ————▶ ?

A	B	C	D	E
0.01	0.02	0.4	0.8	0.04

Question 10

What is the value of $(10 \times 10^3) \div (5 \times 2 \times 10^2)$?

A	B	C	D	E
10	100	1,000	1	0.01

Test 9

Question 11

Liam adds together the factors of 8, and then subtracts the sum of the factors of 6 from the result. What should Liam's answer be?

A	B	C	D	E
3	2	4	5	1

Question 12

What is the difference between the two readings on the thermometers below?

A	B	C	D	E
19°C	11°C	15°C	12°C	13°C

Question 13

The net below forms an open box when folded up. What is the height of the box in millimetres (mm)?

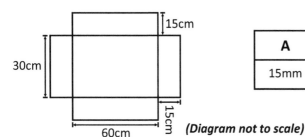

(Diagram not to scale)

A	B	C	D	E
15mm	600mm	150mm	1.5mm	300mm

Question 14

Nishi has 12 red beads, 8 blue beads and 16 green beads. In its simplest form, what is the ratio of red to blue to green beads?

A	B	C	D	E
2 : 4 : 3	3 : 2 : 4	4 : 2 : 3	6 : 4 : 8	8 : 2 : 3

Question 15

If 24 of the 32 children in a class are boys, what percentage of the children are boys?

A	B	C	D	E
80%	70%	75%	65%	50%

Test 9

Question 16

The pictogram below shows the number of meals sold at a cafe over a period of 5 days. How many meals were sold on Wednesday and Thursday?

Number of meals	
Tuesday	🍴 🍴 🍴
Wednesday	🍴 🍴 🍴
Thursday	🍴 🍴 🍴 🍴
Friday	🍴 🍴 🍴 🍴

🍴 = 16 meals

A	B	C	D	E
56	40	92	48	96

Question 17

What is the next term in the sequence below?

1	4	9	16	25	36	?

A	B	C	D	E
41	39	45	49	47

Question 18

Heather is facing northwest (NW) and turns to face southeast (SE). Through what angle has Heather turned?

A	B	C	D	E
45°	270°	315°	90°	180°

Question 19

What is angle $a°$ in the diagram below?

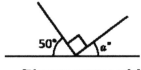

50° $a°$

(Diagram not to scale)

A	B	C	D	E
120°	30°	90°	40°	130°

Question 20

$$a = (b - c) \div d$$

Rearrange the formula above to make b the subject.

A	B	C	D	E
$b = ad + c$	$b = ac - d$	$b = a(d - c)$	$b = cd \div a$	$(ad \div b) + c$

BLANK PAGE

FIRST PAST THE POST®

Numerical Reasoning

Quick Fire Multiple Choice Test 10

Marking Grid																					
Question	1	2	3	4	5	6	7	8	9	10	11	12	13	14	15	16	17	18	19	20	Total
✓ ✗																					/20

Read the following instructions carefully:

1. You have 6 minutes to complete this test of 20 questions.

2. Work as quickly and as carefully as you can.

3. When you have finished a page, go straight onto the next page until you finish the test.

4. You can use all the available space around the question to do your working; however, answer the question by drawing a circle around one of the options provided.

5. To change an answer, either rub it out or put a fine line across your original answer and circle the new answer.

6. If you cannot answer a question, go on to the next question.

7. When you have completed this paper go back to any questions you have missed out and check your answers.

8. Calculators, rulers and protractors are not permitted in this test.

Good luck!

Test 10

Question 1

Add together 0.6m, 20cm and 7mm.

A	B	C	D	E
62.7cm	80.7cm	807cm	8.07m	90.2cm

Question 2

The circular end face (A) of the cylinder below has an area of $9cm^2$. If the volume of the cylinder is $108cm^3$, what is the length (L) of the cylinder?

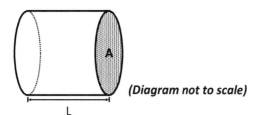

(Diagram not to scale)

A	B	C	D	E
13cm	11.5cm	12.5cm	12cm	11cm

Question 3

What is the missing number n in the expression below?

$$2,742 = 2,000 + 700 + n + 2$$

A	B	C	D	E
42	35	400	4	40

Question 4

What is the input to the number machine below?

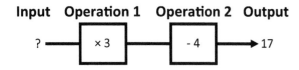

A	B	C	D	E
7	39	63	4	5

Question 5

The ratio of red counters to blue counters in a bag is 7 : 4. If there are 66 counters in total, how many blue counters are in the bag?

A	B	C	D	E
15	24	44	11	42

Test 10

Question 6

The perimeter of an equilateral triangle is 45cm. What is the combined length of two of its sides?

A	B	C	D	E
9cm	30cm	15cm	45cm	15cm^2

Question 7

The container below has a capacity of 4 litres when full. How many millilitres (ml) of water would need to be added to fill the container from $\frac{3}{5}$ full?

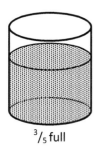

$\frac{3}{5}$ full

A	B	C	D	E
1,000ml	1,600ml	2,000ml	1,500ml	3,000ml

Question 8

If $4p - 8 = p + 4$, what is the value of p?

A	B	C	D	E
$\frac{12}{5}$	1	4	5	3

Question 9

What is the difference between the number of lines of symmetry of a regular octagon and an equilateral triangle?

A	B	C	D	E
-5	7	5	-7	11

Question 10

What is the missing number N in the sequence below?

11   8.5   6   N   1   -1.5

A	B	C	D	E
5	3.5	4.5	2.5	2

Test 10

Question 11

The rectangle R on the grid below is translated 2 squares right and 3 squares down. What are the new coordinates of point P?

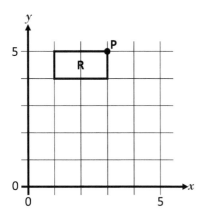

A	B	C	D	E
(5, 3)	(5, 2)	(0, 5)	(5, 0)	(2, 5)

Question 12

What is the value of the 3 in the number 75,326?

A	B	C	D	E
3	30	326	300	0.3

Question 13

Three of the interior angles of a quadrilateral are 70˚, 62˚ and 110˚. What is the 4th interior angle?

A	B	C	D	E
128°	88°	98°	118°	108°

Question 14

What is the lowest common multiple (LCM) of 6, 4 and 8?

A	B	C	D	E
12	16	32	40	24

Question 15

What is angle $c°$ between the hands of the clock shown below?

A	B	C	D	E
30°	45°	25°	35°	50°

Test 10

Question 16

What is the time 8.47pm expressed in 24-hour clock format?

A	B	C	D	E
16:13	20:47	08:47	04:47	12:47

Question 17

The bar chart shows the number of cars sold by a garage in a 3 month period. How many silver and green cars were sold in total?

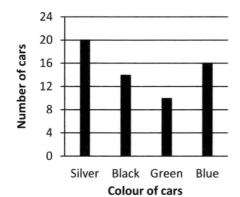

A	B	C	D	E
16	10	14	20	30

Question 18

What is the mode of the set of numbers below?

3 1 7 2 1 5 5 7 2 2 3 7 5 3 7

A	B	C	D	E
1	3	5	2	7

Question 19

The numbers in each row and column in the grid below add up to 38 where each question mark represents a missing number. What is the value of N?

16	?	N
9	?	17
?	8	?

A	B	C	D	E
12	4	22	26	15

Question 20

What is 60% of 15?

A	B	C	D	E
7	7.5	9	15	8

BLANK PAGE

FIRST PAST THE POST®

Numerical Reasoning
Quick Fire Multiple Choice
Book 1
Answers and Explanations

Once you have completed each test and marked it using the answers at the back you can anonymously go online and compare your child's performance relative to peers who have completed the same test(s) using our 11+ Peer Compare System™.

Register at http://peercompare.elevenplusexams.co.uk/ and then activate the access code printed on the front inside cover.

Your unique 16 digit access code is on the inside front cover

Test 1

Question		Answer	Explanation
1	A	21	As $^5/_8$ are playing football, the remaining $^3/_8$ must be playing rugby. Therefore, $^3/_8$ of 56 = 56 × $^3/_8$ = 3 × 7 = 21.
2	B	30	The 3 in the number 4,036 is in the tens column, 3 × 10 = 30.
3	C	17	The product 32 × ? = 544, ? = 544 ÷ 32 = 17.
4		D	Shape D is a square which maps onto itself 4 times during a 360° rotation.
5	E	2, 3, 5	The factors of 30 are: 1, **2**, **3**, **5**, 6, 10, 15, and 30. The prime factors are the factors that are also prime numbers that, when multiplied together, give the original number. Therefore, 2, 3 and 5 are the prime factors of 30.
6	C	24	$a + b$ = 51, 27 + b = 51. Therefore, b = 51 - 27 = 24.
7	E	120cm	2m = 200cm, length per ratio part = 200cm ÷ (3 + 2) = 200cm ÷ 5 = 40cm. Length of longest pipe section = 3 × 40cm = 120cm.
8	C	1,000,000	To change 17.301468 into a whole number, the decimal point needs to be moved 6 places to the right (i.e. multiplied by 1,000,000) to create the number 17,301,468.
9	A	72°	As 18 children prefer peaches and 46 prefer apples, the number of children who prefer oranges is 80 - (18 + 46) = 16. The angle associated with oranges = (16 ÷ 80) × 360° = 72°.
10	E	(9, 7)	From the two known points, the x value changes from 3 to 6 over half the length of the line. Therefore, the x value at end B must be 6 + 3 giving the coordinates (9, 7).
11	A	7	Addition of set numbers ÷ No. in set = mean = (1 + 7 + 2 + ? + 3) ÷ 5 = 4, 13 + ? = 20, ? = 7. As 7 is the number that occurs most in the set, it is the mode.
12	B	24m³	Note that the two wedges when placed on top of each other create a cuboid. Volume of cuboid = 4 × 3 × 2 = 24m³.
13	B	140cm	Length of shape top = $x + 2x + x = 4x$. Perimeter = $4x + 3 × 2x + 4x = 4 × x + 6x + 4x = 14x$. As x represents 10cm, $14x$ = 14 × 10cm = 140cm.
14	D	50°	Angle s° = 180° - 70° = 110° (straight line angle is 180°). Angle t° = 180° - (110° + 20°) = 180° - 130° = 50° (angles in a triangle add to 180°).
15	C	6	The 3rd square number is 9 and the 3rd cube number is 27, sum = 9 + 27 = 36, √36 = 6.
16	A	$^1/_3$	The possible combinations are 1 & 2, 1 & 4, 1 & 6, 2 & 3, 2 & 5, 3 & 4, **3 & 6**, **4 & 5**, **5 & 6** i.e. nine. The combinations that sum to a number > 8 are **3 & 6**, **4 & 5**, **5 & 6**. i.e. Three. Therefore, P(sum > 8) = $^3/_9$ = $^1/_3$.
17		B	Shape B has 8 faces and 6 vertices. Therefore, it has more faces than vertices.
18	E	3hr 34min	**3hr** = 3 × 60min = 180min, 214min - 180min = **34min**. Therefore, 214min = 3hr 34min.
19	A	40m	The scale 1 : 500 tells us that 1cm on the map is 500cm in reality. Therefore, 8cm on the map gives 8cm × 500 = 4000cm in reality. We can convert this into metres by dividing by 100: 4000cm ÷ 100 = 40m.
20	C	3	The sequence is based on doubling numbers. As it is the first term that is missing, halving the second term will result in the first term value i.e. 6 ÷ 2 = 3.

Test 2

Question		Answer	Explanation
1	C	10.6cm	Reading from the ruler scale, nail A = 1.1cm, nail B = 1.8cm and nail C = 2.4cm. 2 × (A + B + C) = 2 × (1.1 + 1.8 + 2.4) = 2 × (5.3) = 10.6cm.
2	A	90%	Percentage = (63 ÷ 70) × 100 = (63 ÷ 7) × 10 = 9 × 10 = 90%.
3	E	5	A symmetrical shape can be divided into two identical mirror images by a line of symmetry. Letter shapes A, H, O, T and X are therefore symmetrical.
4	C	XXX	Note that XVI = 16 and XIV = 14. Therefore, XVI + XIV = 16 + 14 = 30. 30 expressed in Roman numeral form is XXX.
5	E	5.08cm	Cuboid volume (V) = $l \times w \times h$, therefore 10 = 5 × 1 × h, from which height h = 2 inches. As 1 inch = 2.54cm, h = 2 × 2.54cm = 5.08cm.
6	A	0.082	As the 4th decimal number is in the range of a 5 or higher i.e. 6, it is rounded up and the 3rd decimal place increases by 1. Therefore, 0.0816 = 0.082 to 3dp.
7	E	7	$2r + 56 = 10r$. First, subtracting $2r$ from both sides gives $2r - 2r + 56 = 10r - 2r$, which reduces to $56 = 8r$. Dividing both sides by 8 reveals $r = 7$.
8	E	36	The input, 8, is first multiplied by four to give 32. Four is then added to 32 to make 36.
9	B	13:37	2,700s ÷ 60 = 45min. 45min later than 12:52 is 13:37.
10	C	T3	The range of a set of numbers is the difference between the smallest number and the largest number. The greatest range, which is 4°C - (- 5°C) = 9°C, occurs in set T3.
11	D	$^{18}/_{81}$	Multiplying or dividing top and bottom numbers of a fraction by a common number creates an equivalent fraction. $^{18}/_{81}$ is therefore equivalent to $^{2}/_{9}$ i.e. 9 × 2 = 18 and 9 × 9 = 81.
12	C	t = 18, c = 6	Each ratio part = 24 ÷ (3 + 1) = 24 ÷ 4 = 6. Number of teas (t) = 3 × 6 = 18, number of coffees (c) = 1 × 6 = 6.
13	B	7	70 hundreds = 7,000. Number of thousands = 7,000 ÷ 1000 = 7.
14	E	33%	Number of cockroaches = 1,000 - (249 + 251 + 170) = 1,000 - 670 = 330. % of total = (330 ÷ 1,000) × 100 = 330 ÷ 10 = 33%.
15	E	3	A rhombus has 2 pairs of parallel sides and a trapezium has 1 pair of parallel sides. Total number = 2 + 1 = 3.
16	C	(0, -5)	When point Q is rotated from its x-axis position (-5, 0) anticlockwise through 90°, it finishes up on the y-axis below the origin at position (0, -5).
17	D	18cm	Perimeter = $x + x + 2x + 2x = 6x$. As x = 3cm, 6 × 3cm = 18cm.
18	A	2.31L	7 cans hold 7 × 330ml = 2,310ml. Number of litres = 2,310ml ÷ 1,000 = 2.31L.
19	C	$^{2}/_{7}$	Balls with numbers greater than 10 include 11, 12, 13 and 14. Probability P(> 10) = $^{4}/_{14}$ = $^{2}/_{7}$ in its lowest terms.
20	B	864	The product of 24 and 36 = 24 × 36 = 864.

Test 3

Question	Answer		Explanation
1	D	7,000	The 7 in 27,104 is in the thousands column and therefore has a value of 7,000.
2	D	6 and 10	The first 6 triangular numbers are 1, 3, 6, 10, 15 and 21 of which 6 and 10 are even numbers.
3	A	470ml	As there are 1,000ml in 1 litre, 0.47 litres × 1000 = 470ml.
4	B	£2.30	Cost of 10 pencils = 10 × 17p = 170p = £1.70. Cost of pen = £4.00 - £1.70 = £2.30.
5	A	$^1/_2$	As the die is fair, it is equally likely to land on any one of the numbers 1 to 6. Half the numbers available are prime, i.e. (2, 3 and 5), so P(prime) = $^3/_6$ = $^1/_2$.
6	D	4.5	Each sequence term is triple the previous term. The missing term is therefore 3 × 1.5 = 4.5.
7	E	9	Working forwards from the input and applying each instruction in turn gives: Output = (8 ÷ 0.5) - 7 = 16 - 7 = 9.
8	A	4	First, substitute x and y values into the equation $2(x + 4y) = 9z$ to give $2(6 + 4(3)) = 9z$. Next, simplify LHS to give $2(6 + 12) = 9z$, $2(18) = 9z$ and $36 = 9z$. Finally, divide both sides by 9 to give $36 ÷ 9 = 9z ÷ 9$, from which $4 = z$.
9	A	(4, 1)	The mid-point coordinate x value = rectangle length ÷ 2 = (8 - 0) ÷ 2 = 4. The mid-point coordinate y value = rectangle width ÷ 2 = (2 - 0) ÷ 2 = 1. Therefore, the coordinates are (4, 1).
10	C	10	There are 6 small divisions between 12 and 15 on the scale. Each small division is therefore equal to (15 - 12) ÷ 6 = 3 ÷ 6 = 0.5. The total value of 4 small divisions is 2. Therefore, P = 12 - 2 = 10.
11	A	56	The 24 in the second ratio is 8 times the 3 in the first ratio. As the two ratios are equivalent, the value of n must be 8 times the 7 in the first ratio. Therefore, n = 8 × 7 = 56.
12	D	12:00	The flat horizontal section of the graph line indicates the period of time when Pierre took a break at the motorway services, i.e. car stationary. Pierre's break lasted 45 minutes between 11:15 and 12:00. Therefore, Pierre left the services at 12:00.
13	E	54cm^3	Two 3cm wide cubes placed side by side form a cuboid with length = 6cm, width = 3cm and height = 3cm. Volume = 6 × 3 × 3 = 54cm^3.
14	B	(9, 0)	Rotating P 90° anticlockwise from (0, - 9) about (0, 0) moves P from vertically below the origin to the right of the origin at position (9, 0).
15	E	18	The number of vertices on each shape are: 4 (triangular-based pyramid), 6 (triangular prism), 8 (cube). Total number = 4 + 6 + 8 = 18.
16	E	4	The mean of the set = sum of set ÷ number in set = (5 + 1 + 6 + 5 + 3 + 4) ÷ 6 = 24 ÷ 6 = 4.
17	C	108°	As angles in a triangle sum to 180°, the total of the two identical base angles of the isosceles triangle equal 180° - 36° = 144°, each angle being 144° ÷ 2 = 72°. Angle a° = 180° - 72° = 108°.
18	E	60%	Number of counters not red = 40 - 16 = 24. Percentage not red = (24 ÷ 40) × 100 = 60%.
19	A	7cm	Let the width of the rectangle = w, therefore length = $2w$ as length is twice the width. Perimeter = $2w + 2w + w + w = 6w$, 42cm $= 6w$, 42cm $÷ 6 = 6w ÷ 6$, 7cm $= w$.
20	D	One line of symmetry	Kite, Isosceles triangle. From the options available, they all have one line of symmetry in common. Isosceles trapezium.

Test 4

Question		Answer	Explanation
1	A	880	$480 \times 11 = 5280$, $5280 \div 6 = 880$.
2	B	£16	Three-quarters of savings (s) = £12, therefore $3s \div 4 = £12$, $3s = 4 \times £12$, $3s = £48$, $s = £16$.
3	C	6	Work backwards from the output applying the inverse number operations in order. Therefore, $50 \div 5 = 10$, $10 + 8 = 18$, input $n = 18 \div 3 = 6$.
4	B	£15	Individual cost total = £380 + £70 = £450. Combined cost = £435 Individual total is £15 more as £450 - £435 = £15.
5	C	37,020	'Thirty-seven thousand and twenty' in numbers is $37,000 + 20 = 37,020$.
6	C	1, 2, 3, 6, 9, 18	As a factor is a whole number that divides exactly into another number, 1, 2, 3, 6, 9 and 18 are all factors of the number 18.
7	A	14	The number x trebled = $3x$, subtracting 17 gives $3x - 17$ and $3x - 17 = 25$. Solving for x gives $3x = 25 + 17$, $3x = 42$, $x = 42 \div 3 = 14$.
8	B	31	-24°C is 24°C below 0°C and 7°C is 7°C above 0°C. The number of degrees that -24°C is below 7°C is therefore $24 + 7 = 31$.
9	E	39	The pattern follows a number sequence with a common difference of 7 between the terms. Adding 7 to the previous term, 32, in the bottom row gives $32 + 7 = 39$ for the missing term.
10	D	$^{16}/_{25}$	In fraction form, $0.64 = {}^{64}/_{100} = {}^{32}/_{50} = {}^{16}/_{25}$ in its lowest terms.
11	C	18	Observe from the graph that the 09:00 bar ends halfway between 16 and 20 i.e. number of bicycles passing = 18.
12	C	Scalene triangle	The sides of a **scalene triangle** are of different lengths and the 3 angles are all different.
13	E	102°	Opposite angles in a parallelogram are equal and all 4 angles sum to 360°. As two 78° sum to 156°, the other two angles sum to $360° - 156° = 204°$. Angle $a° = 204° \div 2 = 102°$.
14	D	$^{3}/_{5}$	Of the 5 balls numbered 1, 2, 3, 4 and 5, three of them have odd numbers. Therefore, probability of selecting an odd numbered ball P(odd) = $^{3}/_{5}$.
15	C	15	Value of one ratio part = $27 \div (5 + 4) = 3$. Number of boys in class = $5 \times 3 = 15$.
16	C	20cm²	Base of triangle = $5 \times 2cm = 10cm$, height of triangle = $2 \times 2cm = 4cm$. Area of triangle = $^{1}/_{2}$ base × height = $(10 \times 4) \div 2 = 40 \div 2 = 20cm^2$.
17	C	24	A octagonal prism has 8 edges at each end and a further 8 edges along its length. Total number = $8 + 8 + 8 = 24$.
18	C	(3, 8)	As the x-values at A(3, 2) and B(3, 9) are the same and the y-values are different, the line must be vertical. Only (3, 8) can be another point on the line as it has the same x-value and a y-value between 2 and 9, i.e. 8.
19	E	5	The order of rotational symmetry of an equilateral triangle is 3 as it maps onto itself 3 times when rotated through 360°. A rhombus has 2 lines of symmetry. Sum = $3 + 2 = 5$.
20	A	13:40	Three-quarters of an hour before 2.25pm is 1.40pm which is 13:40 in 24-hour clock format.

Test 5

Question		Answer	Explanation
1	A	$6\,^5/_8$	8 goes into 53 six times, i.e. **6** × 8 = 48, with a remainder of 5. As a mixed number this is expressed as $6\,^5/_8$.
2	A	**3.7**	The 6 in 3.68 is in the tenths column, and as the 8 to the right is greater than 4, the 6 is increased by 1 and the 8 discarded giving 3.7 to the nearest tenth.
3	A	**14**	£2.52 × 100 = 252p. Number of 18p pencils = 252p ÷ 18p = 14.
4		**C**	The mirror image appears on the right of the mirror line M and the same distance away.
5	E	**12**	The multiples of 2 are 2, 4, 6, 8, 10, **12** and so on; the multiples of 4 are 4, 8, **12**, 16 and so on and the multiples of 6 are 6, **12**, 18 and so on. The smallest common multiple of 2, 4, and 6 is therefore 12.
6	A	**0**	Working backwards from the output through Operation 2 and changing the sign from + to − gives 78 - 78 = 0. For the output of Operation 1 to be 0, Operation 1 instruction must be × 0 as 29 × 0 = 0.
7	A	**408**	Each ratio part = 1,836 ÷ (7 + 2) = 1,836 ÷ 9 = 204. Population of island Q = 2 × 204 = 408.
8	D	**6.606**	Highest to lowest order is 6.666, **6.606**, 6.60, 6.06 and 6.006. Therefore, the second highest is 6.606.
9	C	**36**	The only number of the four given that is both a square number and a triangular number is 36.
10	B	**(3, 2)**	As point P is reflected in the y-axis, its y-value will remain the same at 2. Its x-value will change from -3 (left of the origin) to +3 (right of the origin). Reflected P = (3, 2).
11	B	**4**	The median is the middle number when the numbers are put in order of size. Writing the set in size order gives 1, 2, 3, **4**, 5, 5, 8. The median is therefore 4.
12	D	**94cm³**	As end area is 9.4cm², prism volume = end area × length = 9.4cm² × 10cm = 94cm³.
13	E	**$4x + 27$**	Single pencil cost = x. As a pen costs 9p more than a pencil, single pen cost = $x + 9$. Cost of 1 pencil and 3 pens = $x + 3(x + 9) = x + 3x + 27 = 4x + 27$.
14	B	**T**	Line T is the only line that is at 90°, i.e. perpendicular to line Q.
15	C	**2012**	The Roman numeral M = 1,000, X = 10 and I = 1. Therefore, MMXII = 1,000 + 1,000 + 10 + 1 + 1 = 2,012.
16	E	$^2/_3$	Possible outcomes from a fair six-sided dice when rolled are 1, 2, 3, 4, 5 or 6. Probability of **not** getting a 2 or a 4 means P(1, 3, 5, 6), i.e. four chances out of six, $^4/_6 = ^2/_3$.
17	B	**1 and 5**	When folded, net A creates a triangular pyramid and net E creates a square pyramid.
18	A	**12**	As there are 30 days in the month of June, there are 5 days between 26th and 30th. The 1st to 7th July = 7 days. Total number of days on holiday = 5 days + 7 days = 12 days.
19	E	**1.4kg**	There are 20 small divisions between 1kg and 2kg. Each small division therefore has a value of 1kg ÷ 20 = 0.05kg. The reading is 1kg + 8 small divisions of 0.05kg = 1kg + 0.4kg = 1.4kg.
20	E	**0.05**	Using the first two terms as an example, the common difference = 1.30 - 1.25 = 0.05.

Test 6

Question		Answer	Explanation
1	C	47.5cm^2	Area of rectangle = $l \times w$ = 10 × 4.75 = 47.5cm^2.
2	B	8 $^5/_6$	53 ÷ 6 = 8 with a remainder of $^5/_6$, hence, 8 $^5/_6$.
3	E	22	Two heptagons have 2 × 7 = 14 sides. One octagon has 8 sides. Therefore, 14 + 8 = 22.
4	E	12	Subtract 21 from both sides: 21 - 21 + x = 45 - x - 21. Simplifiy: x = 24 - x. Add x to both sides: $x + x$ = 24 - x + x. Simplify: $2x$ = 24. Divide both sides by 2 to leave x = 12.
5	B	NW	Turning 45˚ clockwise from SW moves to W, a further 45˚ clockwise moves to NW.
6	E	6.5	As there is an even amount of numbers in the set, the median is half the sum of the two centre numbers. The ascending order of the number set is 1, 2, 5, 6, 7, 7, 8, 11. Therefore, the median is (6 + 7) ÷ 2 = 13 ÷ 2 = 6.5.
7	B	28	Value per ratio part = 63 ÷ (4 + 5) = 63 ÷ 9 = 7. Number of boys = 4 × 7 = 28
8	E	8	Working backwards from the output and using opposite signs, input = 56 ÷ 7 = 8.
9	D	13	3 × (8 - 3) + $\sqrt{49}$ - 3^2 = 3 × 5 + 7 - 9 = 15 + 7 - 9 = 22 - 9 = 13.
10	D	5cm	Volume of a cube = $l \times w \times h$. Substitute in the values: 60cm^3 = 4cm × 3cm × h. Simplify: 60cm^3 = 12cm^2 × $h$cm. Divide both sides by 12cm^2. Hence, 60cm^3 ÷ 12cm^2 = $h$cm, $h$cm = 5cm.
11	E	6	A triangular pyramid has 6 edges.
12	E	64.7cm	To convert from mm to cm, divide by 10. This gives 647 ÷ 10 = 64.7cm.
13	D	1.8kg	Each small division on the scale is worth 1kg ÷ 20 = 0.05kg. The arrow is pointing to 4 small divisions before 2kg. The reading is therefore = 2kg - 0.2kg = 1.8kg.
14	C	$^8/_{10}$	The 8 in the number 42.86 is in the tenths column. This represents $^8/_{10}$.
15	A	160	The bus sector has an angle of 360° - (90° + 30°) = 240°. As 90° represents 60 students, 30° represents 20 students. 240° ÷ 30° = 8. Therefore, 8 × 20 students = 160 students.
16	E	16:28	To convert an afternoon time in 12-hour clock format into 24-hour clock format, add 12 hours. This gives 4.28 + 12 = 16:28.
17	B	$^1/_3$	The fair die has six sides with the numbers 1, 2, 3, 4, 5 and 6. Numbers 1 and 4 are square numbers. Therefore, P(square number) = $^2/_6$ = $^1/_3$.
18	D	(6, 4)	As the two top corners are at (3, 7) and (9, 7) and the square is 6cm wide, the centre x value is given by (9 + 3) ÷ 2 = 6. Since the shape is a square the two bottom corners must have the coordinates (3, 1) and (9, 1). The centre y value is given by (7 + 1) ÷ 2 = 4. Therefore, the coordinates of the centre point are (6, 4).
19	B	10	A regular decagon is a symmetrical shape with 10 sides. It will also map onto itself 10 times when rotated through 360°.
20	A	30%	The shape is made up of 20 small squares, 6 of which are shaded. The percentage of squares that are shaded = (6 ÷ 20) × 100% = 0.3 × 100% = 30%.

Test 7

Question		Answer	Explanation
1	A	5,400	As the 358 in 5,358 is closer to 400 than 300, the number is rounded up to 5,400.
2	C	18cm	Perimeter = (2 × 6cm) + (2 × 3cm) = 12cm + 6cm = 18cm.
3	D	40°	3rd angle = 180° - (70° + 70°) = 180° - 140° = 40°.
4	B	7	Working backwards from the output and using opposite signs, 42 + 7 = 49 then 49 ÷ 7 = 7.
5	A	14	A triangular pyramid has 4 faces, 6 edges and 4 vertices. Total = 4 + 6 + 4 = 14.
6	B	$^1/_3$	Cube numbers in the set are 8 and 27. Therefore, P(cube) = $^2/_6$ = $^1/_3$.
7	A	0	Any number multiplied by 0 = 0. Therefore, the answer is 0.
8	E	(7, 3)	From the x-values of the bottom corner coordinates, the top and bottom sides each have a length of 6 - 2 = 4 units. Hence, the x-coordinate at corner C = 3 + 4 = 7. The y-coordinate at corner C = 3 (i.e. same as top left corner). The answer is C = (7, 3).
9	C	1,000cm^3	Volume = $l \times w \times h$ = 10 × 10 × 10 = 1,000cm^3.
10	D	14	The bottom row is missing the number 5 as 3 + 5 = 8 which is the number above. The middle row is missing the number 6 as 5 + 1 (from the bottom row) = 6. The top row is missing the number 14 as 8 + 6 (from the middle row) = 14.
11	D	6.2	Dividing 1 by 5 in the fraction $^1/_5$ gives 0.2 as a decimal fraction. Therefore, 6 $^1/_5$ = 6.2.
12	C	9	7 children own a cat only and 2 children own a cat and a dog. Therefore, 7 + 2 = 9.
13	B	12	The second term is 1 less than the first term. The third term is 2 less than the second term. This pattern continues throughout. Therefore, the fifth term is 4 less than the fourth term. Hence, the fifth term is 16 - 4 = 12.
14	C	11:08	23 minutes later than 10.45am is 11.08am. This is 11:08 in 24-hour clock format.
15	B	40%	The numbers 7 and 23 are prime numbers. Therefore, the percentage of prime numbers = $^2/_5$ × 100% = 0.4 × 100% = 40%.
16	B	2 : 3	Cancelling down the ratio 24 : 36 by dividing both sides by 12 gives an equivalent ratio of 2 : 3.
17	A	(2, 0)	The x-coordinate of -3 shifts five units to the right to 2. The y-coordinate of 4 shifts four units down to 0. Therefore, the coordinates are (2, 0).
18	B	450ml	There are 10 divisions on the jug, so each division represents 1,500ml ÷ 10 = 150ml. The water level on the scale is 450ml (3 divisions).
19	E	17mm	The scale reading on the ruler is 1.7cm. To convert to mm, multiply by 10: 1.7cm × 10 = 17mm.
20	D	14	First, multiply out the bracket: $3x + 21 = 63$. Then subtract twenty-one from both sides: $3x + 21 - 21 = 63 - 21$ which simplifies to give $3x = 42$. Finally, divide both sides by three: $3x \div 3 = 42 \div 3$ which simplifies to give $x = 14$.

© 2016 ElevenPlusExams.co.uk

Test 8

Question		Answer	Explanation
1	D	6	$3^2 + 3^3 = 9 + 27 = 36$, $\sqrt{36} = 6$.
2	B	28 units^2	From x-coordinate values, rectangle length = 12 - 5 = 7 units From y-coordinate values, rectangle width = 6 - 2 = 4 units. Area = 7 × 4 = 28 units^2.
3	E	G	Line G is at 90° to line A and is therefore perpendicular.
4	A	2 : 3	Red to blue counter ratio is 8 : 12. Dividing the ratio parts by 4 gives an equivalent ratio of 2 : 3.
5	B	23	Number of vertices of a pentagonal prism, a cube and a square pyramid is 10, 8 and 5 respectively. Therefore, the total is given by 10 + 8 + 5 = 23 vertices.
6	C	10	0.1 × 0.1 = 0.01, 0.01 × 1,000 = 10.
7	D	5	$5^3 = 125$. Therefore, $x = 5$.
8	E	0.012kg	To convert from mg to kg divide by 1,000,000. Therefore 12,000mg ÷ 1,000,000 = 0.012kg.
9	C	Wednesday	As there are 30 days in June, the 30th June is a Tuesday. The 8th July is therefore 8 days after the Tuesday which is the following Wednesday.
10	A	$^2/_{13}$	There are 4 aces and 4 Kings in a pack of 52 cards and therefore 8 chances of selecting 1 at random. P(A or K) = $^8/_{52}$ = $^4/_{26}$ = $^2/_{13}$ in its lowest terms.
11	E	-2.3°C	1.4°C - 3.7°C = -2.3°C.
12	D	45	1m = 100cm, 100cm ÷ 20cm = **5**, 60cm ÷ 20cm = **3** and 60cm ÷ 20cm = **3**. Maximum number of 20cm wide cubes is therefore 5 × 3 × 3 = 45.
13	C	45°	As two of the sides are of equal length, the two smaller angles must also be equal. The sum of the two smaller angles sum to 180° - 90° = 90°. Therefore, the smaller angle = 90° ÷ 2 = 45°.
14	A	£2.03	1 loaf of bread costs £1.05 = 105p, 2 pints of milk costs 2 × 49p = 98p. Total cost = 105p + 98p = 203p = £2.03.
15	A	12.8 km per hour	Reading from the graph, distance covered in 30 minutes is 6.4km. Distance covered in 1 hour is 2 × 6.4km = 12.8km. Therefore, speed = 12.8km per hour.
16	D	51cm	A pentagon has 5 sides and a nonagon has 9 sides. Combined perimeter = (5 × 3cm) + (9 × 4cm) = 15cm + 36cm = 51cm.
17	A	160	Multiples of 32 are 32, 64, 96, 128, **160**, ... Multiples of 20 are 20, 40, 60, 80, 100, 120, 140, **160**, ... Therefore, the lowest common multiple (LCM) = 160.
18	E	3x + 4	Pierre is x years old, Pierre's mother is 3 times older i.e. 3x years old. As Pierre's father is 4 years older than his mother, father is 3x + 4 years old.
19	B	8	Factors of 24 are 1, 2, 3, 4, 6, **8**, 12 and 24. Factors of 32 are 1, 2, 4, **8**, 16 and 32. Therefore, the highest common factor (HCF) = 8.
20	E	28	The pattern follows a sequence of triangular numbers. Number of circles required for the 7th term is 28, note the first 7 terms which are 1, 3, 6, 10, 15, 21 and **28**.

Test 9

Question		Answer	Explanation
1	E	23	A prime number has only two factors which are 1 and itself. The next prime number after 19 is therefore 23. See page 2 for a list of special numbers.
2	C	$^3/_5$	As 15 of the 25 circles are shaded, the fraction shaded is $^{15}/_{25}$ which simplifies to $^3/_5$ in its simplest form.
3	A	64	A number multiplied by itself twice results in a cube number. The only cube number between 30 and 120 is 64 from $4 \times 4 \times 4$. See page 2 for a list of special numbers.
4	E	21m^3	Volume of wedge = volume of cuboid ÷ 2 = $(7m \times 3m \times 2m) \div 2 = 42m^3 \div 2 = 21m^3$.
5	D	2	A hexagonal prism has 8 faces, 12 vertices and 18 edges. Therefore, the answer is given by 8 (faces) + 12 (vertices) - 18 (edges) = 2.
6	C	9cm^2	Area of rectangle is $6m \times 3m = 18m^2$. Area of white triangle = $^1/_2 \times$ base $\times$ height = $^1/_2 m \times 6m = 9m^2$. Area of shaded sections = $18m^2 - 9m^2 = 9m^2$.
7	B	(6, 0)	Point A is originally at (0, 6) and therefore 6 units vertically up the y-axis from the origin. A 90° clockwise rotation brings it 6 units to the right of the origin along the x-axis, at (6, 0).
8	D	3	Mean = sum of set ÷ number of terms in set = $(3 + 2 + 5 + 4 + 4 + 1 + 2) \div 7 = 21 \div 7 = 3$.
9	E	0.04	Working from the input, $0.2^2 = 0.2 \times 0.2 = 0.04$.
10	A	10	$(10 \times 10^3) \div (5 \times 2 \times 10^2) = (10 \times 1{,}000) \div (10 \times 100) = 10{,}000 \div 1{,}000 = 10$.
11	A	3	Factors of 8 are 1, 2, 4, 8. These sum to $1 + 2 + 4 + 8 = 15$. Factors of 6 are 1, 2, 3, 6 which sum to $1 + 2 + 3 + 6 = 12$. The difference between the sums is $15 - 12 = 3$.
12	A	19°C	Thermometer readings are 13°C and -6°C. Difference is 13°C - (-6°C) = 13°C + 6°C = 19°C.
13	C	150mm	The four outside sections are folded up to form the open box. Therefore, the height of the box is 15cm. To convert into millimetres multiply by 10. Hence, $15cm \times 10 = 150mm$.
14	B	3 : 2 : 4	Ratio is 12 : 8 : 16. Dividing each part of the ratio by 4 reveals the simplest form of 3 : 2 : 4.
15	C	75%	Percentage of boys = $(24 \div 32) \times 100 = (3 \div 4) \times 100 = 3 \times 25 = 75\%$.
16	C	92	A full symbol represents 16 meals, a half symbol 8 meals and a quarter symbol 4 meals. Wednesday meals = 16 + 16 + 8 = 40 meals, Thursday meals = 16 + 16 + 16 + 4 = 52 meals. Therefore, the answer is given by = 40 + 52 = 92 meals.
17	D	49	This is a sequence of square numbers. The next square number after 36 is 49.
18	E	180°	The direction of SE is opposite to NW. Therefore, a turn of 180° is needed. See page 2 for a list of special numbers.
19	D	40°	Angle $a° = 180° - (90° + 50°) = 180° - 140° = 40°$.
20	A	$b = ad + c$	$a = (b - c) \div d$, First, multiply both sides by d to give $ad = b - c$, Finally, add c to both sides to give $ad + c = b$ (or $b = ad + c$).

Question	Answer		Explanation
1	B	80.7cm	As 0.6m = 60cm and 7mm = 0.7cm, total = 60cm + 20cm + 0.7cm = 80.7cm.
2	D	12cm	Volume (V) = end area (A) × length (L). Therefore, L = V ÷ A = 108cm^3 ÷ 9cm^2 = 12cm.
3	E	40	Missing number n is in the tens column and is therefore worth 40.
4	A	7	Working backwards from the output and inverting signs gives (17 + 4) ÷ 3 = 21 ÷ 3 = 7.
5	B	24	Value of each ratio part = 66 ÷ (7 + 4) = 66 ÷ 11 = 6. Number of blue counters = 6 × 4 = 24.
6	B	30cm	As the 3 sides of an equilateral triangle are equal, length of 2 sides = ($^2/_3$) × 45cm = 30cm.
7	B	1,600ml	As the 4 litre container is already $^3/_5$ full, another $^2/_5$ of the container will fill the container. $^2/_5$ of 4 litres = $^2/_5$ × 4 litres = $^8/_5$ = 1.6 litres. To convert 1.6 litres to millilitres, multiply by 1,000 to give 1,600ml.
8	C	4	Subtract p from both sides of the equation 4p - 8 = p + 4 and simplify to leave 3p - 8 = 4. Next, add 8 to both sides of 3p - 8 = 4 and simplify to leave 3p = 12. Finally, divide both sides by 3 and simplify to leave p = 4.
9	C	5	Number of lines of symmetry for a regular octagon is 8 Number of lines of symmetry for an equilateral triangle is 3. Difference is therefore 8 - 3 = 5.
10	B	3.5	The sequence is a descending set of numbers with a difference of 2.5 between adjacent terms. Therefore, missing number N = 6 - 2.5 = 3.5.
11	B	(5, 2)	Translating rectangle (R) two squares to the right moves corner P to (5, 5). Translating rectangle (R) three squares down moves corner P to its final position of (5, 2).
12	D	300	The 3 is in the hundreds column and worth 300.
13	D	118°	As the four interior angles of a quadrilateral sum to 360°. The fourth angle = 360° - (70° + 62° + 110°) = 360° - 242° = 118°.
14	E	24	The multiples of 6 are: 6, 12, 18, **24**, ... The multiples of 4 are 4, 8, 12, 16, 20, **24**, ... The multiples of 8 are: 8, 16, **24**, 32, ... Therefore, lowest common multiple is 24.
15	B	45°	Angle between any two adjacent clock hour times is 360° ÷ 12 = 30°. At 7.30 (pm or am), the hour hand is halfway between 7 and 8. The minute hand is at 6. Therefore, the angle c° between the clock hands is 1.5 × 30° = 45°.
16	B	20:47	As the time is pm, add 12 hours to convert it to 24-hour clock format. 8.47pm + 12 = 20:47.
17	E	30	From the bar chart, 20 silver cars were sold and 10 green cars were sold. Therefore, 20 + 10 = 30.
18	E	7	The number 7 occurs most often and is therefore the mode.
19	B	4	Missing number in the bottom left corner = 38 - (16 + 9) = 13. Missing number in bottom right corner = 38 - (13 + 8) = 17. Therefore, N = 38 - (17 + 17) = 4.
20	C	9	60% of 15 = (60 ÷ 100) × 15 = 0.6 × 15 = 9.

Your Notes